DEFENDING GENESIS

CELEBRATING THE BEST FROM 40 YEARS OF THE WORLD'S MOST WIDELY-READ
CREATION MAGAZINE

Original *Creation* magazine design

Steve Cardno	Rik Hilverts
Kait D'Arcy	Tim Kneipp
Joshua Daymond	Tim Newcombe
Eve Doyle	Emily O'Bree
Nikala Drager	Caleb Salisbury
Amanda Greenslade	Vanessa Scott

Book design

Nikala Drager	Tim Newcombe
Tim Kneipp	Caleb Salisbury

ISBN 978-1-942773-60-3

First edition January 2018

Published by

CREATION
BOOK PUBLISHERS

PO Box 350
Powder Springs, GA, 30127, USA
Phone: 1-800-616-1264

creationbookpublishers.com

For more information on creation/evolution
and the Christian worldview, go to

CREATION.com

TABLE OF CONTENTS

CREATION MAGAZINE:
40 YEARS OF CHANGING LIVES

By **Carl Wieland**, who founded
the magazine in mid-1978.

U PON GRADUATION from medical school in the early
70s, events in my life made the Gospel very real and
pertinent.[1] But my evolutionary education was a huge
roadblock to becoming a Christian. I was in no doubt
that the Bible taught, and Jesus and the Apostles believed in, the
recent creation of a perfect world in six real days, each with an
evening and a morning—and that a real historical Fall of Adam
ruined this perfection. But science was supposedly telling me that
the fossils, with all the death, disease and suffering they portray,
formed over hundreds of millions of years—thus long before any
appearance of mankind. The contradiction was obvious and stark,
and attempts to 'blend' the two were doomed to failure.

That barrier was removed by reading the landmark 1961 book *The Genesis Flood*, after which I devoured any other creation work I could find. Some questions remained, but I realized that the issue (especially in geology) was not about 'the facts' so much as their interpretation. I was 'set free to believe', as others have since described their similar experiences to me.

Countering brainwashing

Not surprisingly, I had a real passion to let others know, too, and enthusiastic conversations soon led to speaking invitations. Reflecting on why I was convinced of evolution at about age 10, I realized it was largely the colourful, glossy presentations of evolutionary 'facts' in popular magazines. Especially influential, perhaps, were the imaginative drawings of certain 'apemen', later virtually all discarded as human ancestors. I saw the need for a glossy, colourful layman's magazine with articles countering the relentless evolutionary messaging (which has only kept increasing since). But nothing like that was being made anywhere.

So, I thought, why not start one? By 1977, I was part of a small committee comprising the first official creation science organization in Australia,[2] with memberships trickling in from other parts of the country. Such a magazine could be part of members' benefits.[3]

That first issue (then called *Ex Nihilo*, Latin for 'out of nothing'[4]) was neither glossy, nor colourful. This black-and-white effort was typed, then (with pictures stuck on) photocopied before being collated, stapled, and edge-bound by hand with unsightly black tape. It truly was an 'ugly duckling', but the longest journey starts with one footstep, and it *was* a start. Over the years, several have told me how hugely encouraging for them even that first rough prototype was in an evolution-soaked world.

A virtuous circle develops

With intensive ministry in Australian churches by dedicated people, subscriptions grew, though at a snail's pace for many years. The first time the ministry could afford any colour printing for the mag was in 1981, and then only for the cover. As circulation increased, some 'spot' (not full) colour became possible on a few inside pages; then more. And then some *full* colour pages. It became a virtuous circle; the more we could afford to improve its 'looks', along with the quality of content, the easier it became to attract and hold subscribers and supporters, which made more colour possible, and so on. Nonetheless, it was nearly 20 years before we managed full colour on every page.

The advances in technology have been enormous, of course. Not that long ago, the text was printed out on long narrow strips, then cut into varying-length pieces by staff and hand-pasted to make the columns. We would have all been stunned to see the typesetting programs taken for granted today, where text automatically flows into the column spaces, and appears on screen with pictures just as the printed page will look.

Creation magazine now has many tens of thousands of subscribers in over 110 countries worldwide—not to mention the digital option, sharable with several others. But such 'success' would nonetheless be fairly meaningless if unaccompanied by that integral part of the 'vision' all along; change in many lives. Dr Don Batten, my friend and successor as head of the Australian ministry, in his piece following, highlights the effect the magazine keeps on having, and in increasing numbers.

Feedback fuels perseverance

Suffice to say that with all the difficulties the ministry faced over the years (including more than one nearly-successful attempt to shut it down), it was such *testimonies* as Dr Don provides (of faith strengthened, witnessing empowered, and most encouraging of all, people converted) that kept us going, 'pressing on' regardless. They came in by mail, email, by telephone, and in person. It was rare for a CMI speaker at a church not to have at least one person spontaneously approach them about the ministry's (especially the magazine's) impact on them.

Perhaps the most important thing to say in response (apart from thanking them for the encouragement), was that their subscription was doing far more than blessing them. By maintaining it and their support in general, another 'virtuous circle' operated: the more subs, the more CMI was able to not only keep the information cutting-edge, but, via ministry engagements and more, help spread its message into many other homes, and around the world.

I trust this selection of timeless articles from over four decades of *Creation* magazine will inspire you to keep blessing others with its message. ■

References and notes

1. As detailed in the book *Beyond the Shadows*.
2. The Creation Science Association (CSA) of South Australia. This was later absorbed into a body that had been emerging in the State of Queensland, the Creation Science Foundation (1980). CSF took over the production and distribution of the magazine early on; I then led it from 1987, having moved to Queensland. In the 1990s it changed its name to Answers in Genesis (Australia) and then in 2006 to *Creation Ministries International* (CMI), the Australian arm of a worldwide Federation of CMI sister ministries who all share the same aims, beliefs, website, publications etc. (see creation.com/contact).
3. It was then more of a 'creation club' than a ministry, something that quickly showed itself as not ideal.
4. The name made it seem more 'technical' than it was, so it was later changed. But since it was already widely loved under the original name, the transition was eased by first changing it to *Creation Ex Nihilo*.

Dr Carl Wieland spent over 40 years in active creation ministry, at first part-time while practising medicine in South Australia. Having commenced Creation *magazine in 1978, he went on to be Managing Director of the ministry producing it (now* Creation Ministries International–Australia*), in 1987. He remained in this role, and was a senior editor of the magazine, until he retired in 2015. For more: creation.com/carl-wieland.*

Ben Goode/123RF

CREATION MAGAZINE:
onward!

Dr Don Batten,
Managing Editor

I COUNT IT as a huge privilege to now be the managing editor of *Creation* magazine. My friend and colleague, Dr Carl Wieland, leaves big shoes to fill. He set an example of publishing integrity that we must strive to maintain so that we continue to effectively equip God's people.

We receive lots of encouragement from *Creation* readers. Their feedback shows that the magazine:

1. **Leads to conversions to Christ.** One of my favourite testimonies came from a man from Gympie in country Queensland, Australia: "I was converted when someone gave me a *Creation* magazine. Then I subscribed for five of my relatives. Four of them have now come to the Lord." Wow! How many evangelists would love to have those percentages? I remember a man contacting us to share how after years of his wife praying for his conversion, he had finally 'come through'. His wife would leave *Creation* magazine lying around the house. When she was not around, he would read them, putting them back exactly as she had placed them, so that she would not know that he had been reading it!

2. **Equips Christians for witnessing and evokes confidence.** John, an 89-year-old gentleman, shared with us that a couple of years previously he and his wife were at a meeting for people who spoke the Cornish language when someone asked him, "How is church going?" A young lady seated at their table piped up with, "Nothing in the Bible is true", and that this had all been proved in a book she had just been reading by one Richard Dawkins. John had subscribed to *Creation* magazine for many years, and he said he refuted every one of her arguments solely using the material he had read in *Creation*. The discussion went for over an hour! She then admitted that John was right! Others seated at the table had gone to church as young people but had not been for many years. At the end of the discussion with John, many of them decided to go back to church, and continue to do so today! And all this because one man had read *Creation* magazines. But note something: John's experience underlines the importance of maintaining a subscription to be continually 'topped up' and fed, keeping up to date; being prepared (1 Peter 3:15).

3. **Provides a straightforward approach to witnessing that anyone can use.** For example, one man shared that, "You make evangelism easy. When I meet someone, I give them a *Creation* magazine, and the next time we meet we talk about it." Many find it difficult to get a Gospel-focused conversation started; *Creation* magazine provides a ready way, even with people who say they are not interested. I remember a young pastor and his wife in New Zealand who had been witnessing to a policeman friend. The good friend was not at all interested in their 'religious' views. They left him baby-sitting their children one evening, deliberately leaving a *Creation* magazine sitting on the coffee table (and nothing else, and no TV!). When they came home he said, "I've been reading that magazine like you meant me to; I've never read anything like that, do you have anything else like that? They gave him further reading and within two weeks he came to faith in Christ. This is common, to hear about even seemingly resistant people, completely opposed, coming to faith.

4. **Helps protect children in Christian families from losing their way** due to today's rampant evolutionary indoctrination. Kerry W. shared how, "creation ministries over the years have contributed to our four children, now all married, all walking in the faith with their spouses, and raising the next generation on a creation foundation." In my own house, my wife and I have been blessed in our three grown children walking with the Lord, and they also benefitted from having *Creation* magazine in the home as they were growing up. It is so colourful that children will pick it up and read the parts that attract their interest, reinforcing to them that the Bible speaks of realities, not just 'stories'. It's difficult to turn your back on Christ when you know that what the Bible says is true and really does fit the facts of the real world.

5. **Helps restore those who have lost their way** through evolutionary indoctrination. We have lots of stories of this. John's account above provides several examples and there are many others. I have met pastors who had been ready to give up pastoring who were restored to a confident faith, getting back into enthusiastic pastoral work.

As Carl has noted, people subscribe to *Creation* from all over the world. Magazine articles have inspired people of other languages to translate them; there are now articles in 40 languages other than English on creation.com, and many of those articles are from past *Creation* magazines.

Keeping up with the times, *Creation* magazine is now available in digital format and when you get your email with the link, you can share it with several others, thus spreading the reach of the message.

With each issue, we endeavour to cover a range of topics so that each issue is to some extent comprehensive in its coverage (and has 'something for everyone'). This means that a new reader will get something that 'covers the bases' in any issue, and articles that will be of personal interest.

Reading this, you are probably a *Creation* magazine subscriber (thank you!). May I encourage you to continue subscribing to *Creation* and sharing it with others? If you are not a subscriber, how about getting on board? As the small sample of stories shared above show, it does 'a power of good', and the good will only multiply as people come on board to share the magazine around. We estimate that each printed magazine is read by five people or more and the digital version extends that reach. If we had 100,000 subscribers, that could reach a million people or more with each issue.

I trust that you will enjoy (and share!) this compilation of 'the best of' *Creation* magazine over the years. Thank-you for being a part of this Gospel enterprise! ∎

DON BATTEN, B.Sc.Agr.(Hons.), Ph.D.
Dr Batten worked as a research scientist and consultant plant physiologist and is now the Managing Director of Creation Ministries International *in Brisbane, Australia. For more:* creation.com/batten.

DID GOD
CREATE OVER
BILLIONS
OF YEARS?
...and why is it important?

Gary Bates and Lita Cosner

OFTEN, PEOPLE challenge biblical creationists with comments such as, "God could have taken billions of years to create, so what's the big deal about the age of the earth?" Some claim that an emphasis on '6 literal days, 6,000 years ago' even keeps people away from the faith, so "Why place a strong emphasis on something that's not a salvation issue?"

Surprisingly, we *agree*—to a point. The timescale *in and of itself* is not the important issue. It ultimately comes down to, "Does the Bible actually mean what it says?" The issue is about the trustworthiness of Scripture—compromising with long ages severely undermines the whole Gospel.

The implications of a long-age timescale

Millions or billions of years are never mentioned anywhere in Scripture; the concept is derived from *outside* of the Bible. In his 1830 book, *Principles of Geology*, Charles Lyell, a Scottish lawyer, argued that the thousands of feet of sedimentary layers (laid down by water or some other moving fluid) all over the earth were the result of long, slow, gradual processes over millions or billions of years. He believed that processes observed in the present must be used to explain the geological history of the earth ('uniformitarianism'). His stated aim was "To free the science [of geology] from Moses."[1]

If we currently see rivers laying down sediment at an average rate of say 1 mm (4/100th of an inch) per year, then a layer of sedimentary rock such as sandstone which is 1,000 meters (3,300 feet) thick is presumed to have taken about a million years to form. This 'present is the key to the past' assumption (and its variants) is a cornerstone of modern geology. It rejects the biblical account of a global watery cataclysm. The millions of years assigned to the various layers in the 'geological column' were adopted long before the radiometric 'dating' methods that supposedly prove them. But here's the theological problem. These layers don't just have rocks or minerals in them. They contain fossils—indisputable evidence of death, carnivory, disease and suffering. Some remains have tooth marks in them, and animals fossilized in the process of eating other animals, and suffering from wounds, broken bones, etc. The Bible teaches that these things only began to happen *after the Fall*. But in a secular timescale, these fossils, with their evidence of death and suffering, existed long before any human. The implication of long-age belief is that God ordained death before the Fall of man, contrary to the Bible's clear teaching that His finished Creation was good, and it was Adam's actions that brought death into the world (Romans 5:12).

The god of an old earth

The idea that God used evolution to create has harmful implications for God's character. Evolution is a random and wasteful process that requires millions of 'unfit' organisms to die. Countless transitional forms become extinct and fall aside as casualties in the great march 'forward'. After this allegedly 'good' God-ordained lottery of death finally resulted in humans, the evolutionary view says that God looked at His image-bearers, standing on top of layers of rocks filled with the remains of billions of dead things, and proclaimed His whole creation—along with the evidence of all the death and suffering that went into creating it—to be 'very good' (Genesis 1:31).

The gospel of an old earth

Some try to sidestep this issue by saying that the Fall only caused *human* death and disease. But Romans 8:19–22 clearly teaches that the curse of death and suffering following Adam's Fall affected "the whole creation", i.e. the entire physical universe.

But even if we set that aside for the sake of argument, there is another problem, because we have human remains 'dated' before the biblical date for Adam, which places him in the Garden about 6,000 years ago (see How does the Bible teach 6,000 years? p. 28). Many compromising positions see these hominid fossils as 'pre-Adamites'—soulless non-human animals. But these skeletons fall within the normal range of human variation. And Neandertals, for example, show signs of art, culture and even religion. Recently, the sequencing of actual Neandertal DNA shows that many of us carry Neandertal genes—i.e. we are the same created kind.[2] To call them 'non-human animals' seems entirely contrived to salvage the long-age belief system.

Romans 8:19–20 tells us the *whole* creation groans under the weight of sin and is subjected to futility. And Genesis 3:17–19 tells us that the very

Article from
Creation **35**(2):50–52
April 2013

DEATH

SUFFERING

DISEASE

ground was cursed so that it produced thorns and thistles.[3] If only a partial Fall occurred, then why will God destroy all creation to bring about a new one instead of a partial restoration? Why not just restore humans if the rest of creation is still "very good"?

Death the last enemy

A central part of the Gospel is that death is the last enemy to be destroyed (1 Corinthians 15:26). Death intruded into a perfect world because of sin, and it is so serious that Jesus' victory over death cannot be entirely manifested while there is a single believer in the grave. Are we expected to believe that something the Bible authors described as an enemy was used or overseen by God for millions of years and was called "very good"?

Christians also have the hope of the Resurrection and restoration of the creation to its original perfect state. The Bible is clear about the New Heavens and Earth as a place where there is no death, no suffering, and no sin (Isaiah 65:17–25; Revelation 21:1–5). But how can this be called a *restoration* if such a state never existed?

An evolutionist Anglican priest gave a good summary of what accepting death before the Fall means for Christian theology:

"Death is as old as life itself by all but a split second. Can it therefore be God's punishment for Sin? ... From the dawn of time, the possibility of life and death, good and evil, have always existed. At no point is there any discontinuity; there was never a time when death appeared, or a moment when the evil [sic] changed the nature of the universe. God made the world as it is ... People try to tell us that Adam had a perfect relationship with God until he sinned, and all we need to do is repent and accept Jesus in order to restore that original relationship. But perfection like this never existed. There never was such a world. Trying to return to it, either in reality or spiritually, is a delusion."[4]

This clearly shows the logical end of allowing for billions of years, with or without evolution. Its logical corollary is that there was also evil before the Fall—indeed, there's no longer anywhere to fall from. And in the process it rules out the hope of a return to a perfect state, since there can be no return to what never was. The Gospel itself has been destroyed in the process.

The effect on the church

A major stumbling block to faith is: "Why does a good God allow all the death and suffering in the world?" Christians who accept death before the Fall cannot adequately explain the origin of death and suffering as a reaction to human sin. Their ability to defend their faith is severely compromised.

Conversely, believers who have a biblical view of the world's history have a logical platform for introducing God to people with no scriptural background.

Incidentally, this was precisely the approach that Paul used when preaching to similar Gentile audiences (Acts 14:15–17; 17:23–31).

Most Christian leaders and theologians who lay out their reasons for believing in long ages have to admit that Genesis teaches a straightforward creation in six normal-length days. Unfortunately they accept that science has somehow 'proved' millions of years, which is actually not the case.

Inconsistent Christianity?

While it is possible to be a Christian and believe in an old earth, it would indicate that one has not thought through the consequences. If Genesis is not real literal history, how can one know where the truth actually does begin in Scripture? Today's 'science' also 'proves' that men don't rise from the dead.

Jesus said, "If I have told you earthly things and you do not believe, how can you believe if I tell you heavenly things?" (John 3:12). And because Jesus clearly believed in a literal historical Genesis, so should we. ∎

References and notes

1. Charles Lyell, personal letter to George Poulett Scrope, 14 June 1830; see creation.com/Lyell.
2. Carter, R.W., The Neandertal mitochrondial genome does not support evolution, *J. Creation* **23**(1):40–43, 2009; creation.com/neandertal-mitochondrial-genome.
3. Interestingly, the fossil record contains thorns. A conventional interpretation of the fossil record (which denies the global Flood) places them at 'hundreds of millions' of years before any human being. See W.N. Stewart and G.W. Rothwell, *Paleobotany and the Evolution of Plants* (Cambridge, UK: Cambridge University Press, 1993), p. 172 – 176.
4. Tom Ambrose, 'Just a pile of old bones', *The Church of England Newspaper*, A Current Affairs section, 21 October 1994.

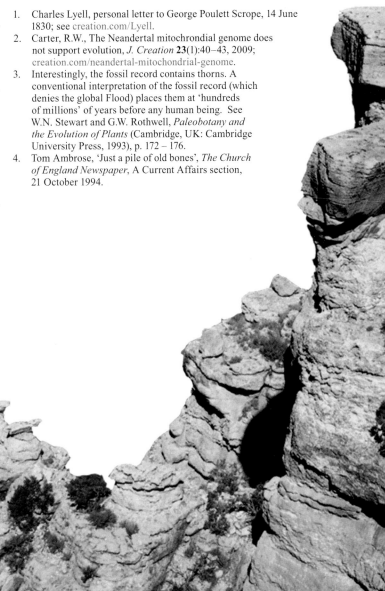

WHAT SHOULD A CHRISTIAN THINK ABOUT EVOLUTION?

Prof. J. Rendle-Short

I HAVE every sympathy with those who find this question difficult to answer. In my teens, I believed that creation was true, but during my University years and afterwards I began to compromise. I became a theoretical creationist on Sundays, and a practical evolutionist for the rest of the week. In practice, I thought little about the matter, although it remained a mild irritant in the background. Later I worked out a fairly comfortable position as a theistic evolutionist—that is, I accepted the evolutionary theory as true, but wherever an atheist would write 'chance', I would substitute 'God' or 'Providence'. How man and animals evolved, I did not know, but I was certain that whatever means had been used, God was in control. Recently, however, the evidence has compelled me to become a creationist. I say compelled because my whole medical training and indeed all that I hear from day to day in books and the media, shouts evolution at me. It is hard to abandon the thought processes of a lifetime.

This recent change of opinion has not occurred because I discovered creation to be more scientifically credible than evolution. Even convinced evolutionists find it difficult to account for the origin of the worlds from nothing and of life from primordial slime; they wonder at the complexity and beauty of design in nature, as they often acknowledge by giving the word a capital 'N'—Nature. I am a creationist because I believe that Creation alone conforms to the total thrust of Scripture as it is unfolded from Genesis to Revelation, and particularly as the Gospel is revealed in the New Testament.

Most devout Christians ask, 'But does it matter? Why rock the boat? The battle, creation versus evolution, was fought (and lost) by previous generations of Christians. Why bring it up now?' But it *does* matter, for the following reasons:

(If you are a Christian please ponder this deeply with an open Bible and prayer.)

1. Genesis 1–9 purports to be history rather than poetry or mythology. Writers throughout Scripture, particularly in the Psalms and the New Testament, treat it as history, as did our Lord. Genesis is more quoted in the rest of the Bible than any other book. If the early chapters of Genesis are allegory, what about the walls of Jericho, Jonah and the great fish, the virgin birth, and the resurrection of Christ? At what point do you say, 'But that I can't believe?'

2. Unless the world was originally created 'very good', it is difficult to

see how man could 'fall'. From what state did he fall? If Adam was derived from some pre-existing hominoid, then what is the significance of sin? If there was no historic fall, why is there need of a Saviour?

3. Adam was told that the penalty for sin would be death, but what thrust had that if millions of animals, including hominoids, had died over thousands of years? In both Old and New Testaments sin is repeatedly coupled with death: "The wages of sin is death," (Romans 6:23). Adam's sin is specifically linked with death in Romans 5 and 1 Corinthians 15. In the latter passage, it is certain that physical death is intended, because it is compared with the indisputably physical death and Resurrection of Christ. If death occurred before Adam sinned the total Gospel is negated, including our hope of the Resurrection.

4. The evolutionary method involving violence, pain and death is totally out of keeping with the character of God as revealed in Scripture. Our God is a God of joy, peace and love. He destroyed the Earth at the time of Noah because it was filled with violence. The LORD said, "I will blot out man whom I have created from the face of the land, man and animals and creeping things and birds of the heavens, for I am sorry that I have made them" (Genesis 6:7). It is noteworthy that it was the violence of animals as well as man that God deplored.

5. Atheistic evolutionists have difficulty accounting for altruism. Where do love and philanthropy come from in a world evolving by chance mutation and natural selection? Theistic evolutionists have a problem too. If God used the evolutionary method, then He is the author of pain and suffering and evil. God becomes a devil. Only an initially perfect world, created by a loving God but ruined by the entrance

of sin, can account for *both* the good and evil which we find around us.

6. The origin of many basic doctrines can be traced to the first chapters of Genesis. For example, it is impossible for the narrative of the creation of Eve and out of Adam—woman out of man—to be anything other than fanciful mythology or historic truth. At least seven fundamental Biblical doctrines are linked with the last three verses of Genesis 2, the passage which recounts the creation of Eve:

If Eve was born *per via naturalis,* from some pre-existing animal, then all these doctrines are based on a misleading myth.

Relationship between man and woman
1 Corinthians 11:3, 8, 9; Ephesians 5:22–24

Women in the church
1 Tim. 2:11–13

Marriage as one man and one woman
Matthew 19:4–9

Divorce
Matthew 19:7-10

Sexual immorality
1 Corinthians 6:16

Husbands to love their wives
Ephesians 5:28–31

Christ's love for His body the Church
Ephesians 5:25–32; 1:22, 23; Col. 1:15–18, 24

---

7. The Judeo-Christian pattern of one day's rest in seven follows directly on the fact that the God created the world was created in six days and rested on the seventh (Genesis 2:2, Exodus 20:11).

8. Evolution (including presumably theistic evolution) is a continuing process. Darwin's book, *The Origin of Species*, was subtitled, *The preservation of favoured races in the struggle for life*. Evolution provides the scientific orthodoxy for the philosophies of fascism, racism, apartheid, and communism.

9. Evolution lowers man from the 'image of God' to the level of an animal. Why

then should he not behave as one, in his own life and towards others?

10. The longevity of Adam, Seth and others (Genesis 5) can be nothing but mythology if evolution were true. Primitive man rarely lived much beyond forty years.

Conclusion

A Christian has the following options:

1. To assume that Genesis 1–9 is allegory, myth or poetry not to be taken literally. But if so, what do we do with the rest of the Bible? Why stop there?

2. To hold on to both creation and evolution and try to reconcile the two. This state is unstable and readily leads to liberalism.

3. To ignore the Old Testament and make an existential leap to a shallow believism.

4. To accept that "by faith we understand that the worlds were made by the word of God" (Hebrews 11:3). Only in this, the scriptural way, do we find release from the tensions of the conflict. ■

PROFESSOR JOHN RENDLE-SHORT (1919–2010), A.M., M.A., M.B., B.Chir., M.D. (Cantab.), F.R.C.P., F.R.A.C.P.
Dr T. (Tyndale) John Rendle-Short was Foundation Professor and for 24 years Head of the Department of Child Health in the University of Queensland, Brisbane, Australia, and a Member of the Order of Australia for his pioneering research in infantile autism. From its founding in 1980, he was for many years also the chairman of the board of the organisation that later became Creation Ministries International (Australia). *For more: creation.com/professor-john-rendle-short.*

Article from
Creation 3(1):15–17
February 1980

Tas Walker

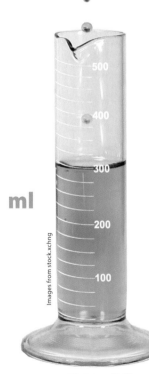

ml

rate=50ml/hour

ADDRESSING THE students, I used a measuring cylinder to illustrate how scientific dating works. My picture showed a water tap dripping into the cylinder. It was clearly marked so my audience could see that it held exactly 300 ml of water. The diagram also showed that the water was dripping at a rate of 50 ml per hour.

I asked, "How long has the water been dripping into the cylinder?"

Immediately someone called out, "Six hours."

"Good. How did you work that out?"

"By dividing the amount of water in the cylinder (300 ml) by the rate (50 ml per hour)."

"Excellent," I said. "See how easy it is to calculate the age of something scientifically? Every dating method that scientists use works exactly the same way. It involves measuring something that is changing with time."

People began to relax once they understood that the science of dating is not so difficult. Then I surprised them, "The problem is that six hours is the wrong answer."

They look puzzled and disbelieving.

"I set this experiment up and I can tell you that the water has only been dripping for *one* hour. Can you tell me what happened?"

After they had composed themselves, someone called out, "The tap was dripping faster in the past?"

"Perhaps," I said.

"The cylinder was nearly full when you started?"

"Maybe. But can you see what you are doing?" I asked. "In order to calculate an age

you made assumptions about the past. You assumed the rate had always been 50 ml per hour and that the cylinder was empty when it started. Based on those assumptions you calculated the time of six hours."

They nodded.

"You were perfectly happy with that answer. Not one of you challenged it." They agreed.

"Then, when I told you the correct answer, do you realize what you did? You quickly changed your assumptions about the past in order to agree with the age I told you."

Every scientist must first make assumptions about the past before he can calculate an age. If the result seems okay then he will happily accept it. But if it does not agree with other information then he will change his assumptions so that his answer does agree.

It does not matter if the calculated age is too old or too young. There are always many assumptions a scientist can make to get a consistent answer.

Suddenly, the lights went on. My audience saw, in a nutshell, the way dating methods work.[1] Scientific dating is not a way of measuring but a way of thinking. ∎

References and notes

1. For further information see: Walker, T., The way it really is: little-known facts about radiometric dating, *Creation* **24**(4):20–23, 2002; creation.com/dating-reality; Sarfati, J., Diamonds: a creationist's best friend, p. 70.

TAS WALKER,
B.Sc.(Hons.) [geology],
B.Eng.(Hons.), Ph.D.
Dr Walker worked in power station design and operation, and the geological assessment of coal deposits. He works full-time researching and speaking for Creation Ministries International (Australia). *For more: creation.com/walker.*

Images from stock.xchng

Article from
Creation **30**(3):28–29
June 2008

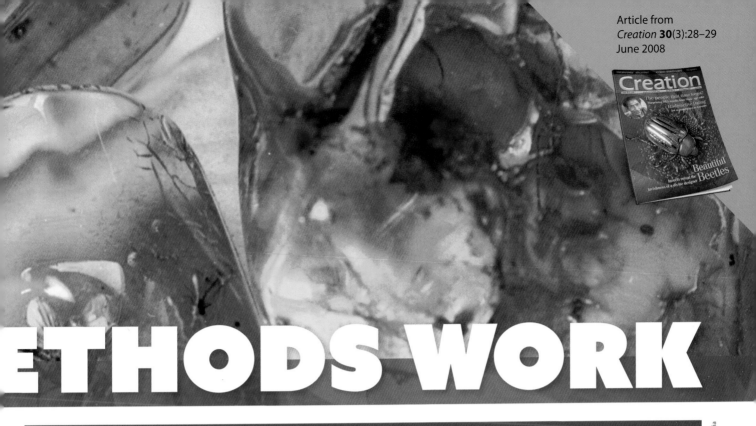

ETHODS WORK

HOW IT WORKS IN PRACTICE

A layer of volcanic ash in East Africa, called the KBS tuff, became famous through the human fossils found nearby.[1]

Using the potassium-argon method, Fitch and Miller were the first to measure the age of the tuff. Their result of 212–230 million years did not agree with the age of the fossils (elephant, pig, ape and tools) so they rejected the date. They said the sample was contaminated with excess argon.[2]

Using new samples of feldspar and pumice they 'reliably dated' the tuff at 2.61 million years, which agreed nicely. Later, this date was confirmed by two other dating methods (paleomagnetism and fission tracks), and was widely accepted.

Then Richard Leakey found a skull (called KNM-ER 1470) *below* the KBS tuff, a skull that looked far too modern to be 3 million years old.

So Curtis and others redated the KBS tuff using selected pumice and feldspar samples, and obtained an age of 1.82 million years. This new date agreed with the appearance of the new skull.[3]

Tests by other scientists using paleomagnetism and fission tracks confirmed the lower date.

So, by 1980 there was a new, remarkably concordant date for the KBS tuff, and this became the one that was widely accepted.

Which illustrates that, contrary to popular belief, the dating methods are not the primary way that ages are decided. The dating methods do not lead but follow. Their results are always 'interpreted' to agree with other factors, such as the evolutionary interpretation of geology and fossils.

References and notes

1. For more information see Lubenow, M.L., The pigs took it all, *Creation* **17**(3):36–38, 1995; creation.com/pigstook.
2. Fitch, F.J. and Miller, J.A., Radioisotopic age determinations of Lake Rudolf artifact site, *Nature* **226**(5242):226–228, 1970.
3. Curtis, G.H. *et al.*, Age of KBS Tuff in Koobi Fora Formation, East Rudolf, Kenya, *Nature* **258**:395–398, 4 December 1975.

Replica of skull KNM-ER 1470

Slaying yesterday's Dragons

Robert Carter

DARWINISM AS a science has been evolving. That is, it has changed from its original concept and continues to change. It would do us well to pay attention to the latest trends so as not to be caught arguing against yesterday's theory. When Charles Darwin initially postulated that all living species could be traced back to a single common ancestor, he suggested the mechanism causing these changes was natural selection.[1] That was in 1859. Later, he backed off from his initial hypothesis and suggested that other forms of selection (e.g., sexual selection[2]) were not only involved, but were more important. Worse, not knowing anything about genetics, he came up with and strongly promoted a Lamarckian[3] idea that the environment caused changes in organisms which were then inherited by their offspring. This was contradicted by his contemporary, Gregor Mendel, who published the laws of genetics[4] in 1862, but that was the state of evolutionary theory at the close of the 19th century.

More changes occurred when genetics was finally brought under the Darwinian umbrella in the early 20th century. This involved a wholesale rejection of much of Darwin's later writings and eventually led to the 'Modern Synthesis' of evolution, genetics, and population genetics under which most biologists today were trained. This 'gene-centric' view dealt with populations and gene pools, ignoring the fact that the individual (a complex combination of traits) was the unit of selection and not individual genes. Proponents of this view also ran into mathematical difficulties[5] early on, but these were pushed aside by further speculation that most of the genome was junk DNA.[6]

Now that we have entered the 21st century, things are changing once again. As we have learned more about genetics and the inner workings of the cell, neo-Darwinism (another name for the Modern Synthesis) is having to adapt. Evolutionists have had a difficult time explaining incredibly complex systems like the human genome, and the naturalistic origin of life flies in the face of all known laws of physics, chemistry, genetics, probability, and information theory. The idea that most of our DNA is 'junk'[6] is now untenable. The mathematical difficulties discovered decades ago are only getting worse as our understanding of life becomes more and more complex. What is an evolutionist to do?

Thomas Kuhn, a famous philosopher of science, said that scientific revolutions occur every several generations. When a new theory rises to the top, it is

promoted heavily. The next generation of scientists runs with it, often using it as a basic assumption of how things work. Eventually, however, enough cognitive dissonance[7] is raised, especially among the younger scientists who often find older ideas unsatisfactory, that a whole-sale turnover of ideas occurs. For example, the phlogiston theory of combustion once ruled academia, but a few experiments in the late 1700s put an end to it. Another revolution occurred in the 1960s when plate tectonics suddenly replaced a geology based on static continental blocks. A scientific theory tends to have a certain amount of inertia and it takes a considerable effort to change it once it is established as a ruling paradigm, but it *can* change.

Will another revolution occur in evolutionary theory? Probably so, and we can see early rumblings of it already. This is not to say that lots of scientists are going to become biblical creationists, but that there are a significant number of people in science who are less than satisfied by mainstream ideas of how evolution works. We can see young scientists pushing the pagan-esque Gaia hypothesis[8] and others talking about nebulous self-organizing properties supposedly inherent in matter that drive evolution inexorably forward.[9] There is a Kuhnian[10] revolution in the works, no doubt. The movers and shakers of the new revolution, though, are leaving mathematics and population genetics (because these failed Darwin and because the problems have not been resolved by neo-Darwinism, i.e. the Modern Synthesis) and are turning to more philo-sophically speculative ideas.

Things are shifting under our feet. We need to be careful not to be caught slaying yesterday's dragon. Yet, the new trends within science do not necessarily require a different type of counter-argument. Interestingly, I find myself arguing population genetics as a cogent weapon when confronted by these newer ideas. I find myself talking about what we *know* about physics and chemistry and how that contradicts all ideas about the physical origin of life from non-life. I find myself saying that what we have discovered through experimental science argues against there being any inherent property in matter that would drive it to spontaneously form high-level organizational structures, let alone codified information strings.[11] It is as if they are suddenly admitting to a 'Darwin of the Gaps' model of evolution while we creationists stick to empirical science, and I find this ironic, even oddly humorous.

Although evolutionary theory is threatening to change its basis, the argument has not really changed all that much. Why is this?

Because evolution is a smokescreen for a raging spiritual battle. The *how* of evolution is really not all that important, and evolutionists will readily shift their beliefs about the mechanism behind it, often using these shifts to claim science is self-correcting. The alleged *fact* of evolution, however, must be defended by its adherents at all costs, because there is no escape from accountability to a Creator unless nature made itself somehow.

Although this shift away from neo-Darwinism is certainly not yet the majority view, it is a rapidly popularizing trend within science. It seems, therefore, as if the big question we are going to face in the future is similar to one faced when trying to share the Gospel with the new generation of public school kids (you know, the ones that could not say that taking down the Twin Towers was an act of evil men). That is, how do you talk to a science buff who has left empirical science and whose mind is full of philosophical speculation?

In short, there is, to this point, no coherent science coming from this new paradigm of neo-pagan metaphysics with nature as a self-creating entity, demonstrating that the battle is really being waged at a deeper philosophical level. Therefore, the creationist arguments that have been developed over the past several decades remain relevant and powerful. Resources like *The Creation Answers Book*, creation.com, *Journal of Creation* and *Creation* magazine are still the best sources of information one can use to prepare a defence, for there is nothing truly new under the sun. ∎

References and notes

1. See articles in our Q&A page creation.com/selection.
2. Catchpoole, D., creation.com/peacock-poppycock, March 2007.
3. Carter, R., creation.com/epigenetics-and-darwin, 1 March 2011.
4. Lester, L., creation.com/genetics-no-friend-of-evolution, March 1998.
5. Batten, D., creation.com/Haldane, April 2005.
6. Carter, R., creation.com/junkdnadeath, 9 June 2009.
7. This term refers to the holding of conflicting beliefs, and the tension/discomfort this causes.
8. Wieland, C., creation.com/pagan-panic, December 1992.
9. Depew, D. and Weber, B., The fate of Darwinism: evolution after the modern synthesis, *Biological Theory* **6**(1):89-102, 2011.
10. Kulikovsky, A., creation.com/johncollins2, December 2007.
11. Gitt, W., creation.com/laws-of-information-1, August 1996.

Article from
Creation **35**(3):12–14
July 2013

Article from
Creation **7**(1):20
June 1984

THE PITCH FOR NOAH'S ARK

Tas Walker

MANY GEOLOGISTS claim that Noah could not possibly have built the ark in the manner described in Genesis. They argue that pitch could not have been used to cover the ark and make it waterproof. Pitch, they claim, is derived from oil or coal, and if coal did not form until during the time of Noah's Flood, he could not possibly have covered the ark with pitch.

For those who are not geologists, pitch is a black glue-like substance left behind when coal tar is heated or distilled. It belongs to the same family of substances as asphalt or bitumen. Today, it is largely produced by heating coal. Most modern geologists know of no other source for it. But coal tar and petroleum are not the only source for pitch. Anyone who takes the time to consult a reasonable dictionary of geology will find that pitch can be extracted by distilling or heating wood. In fact, prior to the rise of the petroleum and coal industries, this was exactly how pitch was made.

For at least one thousand years, the pitch-making industry in Europe flourished. It was the pitch from this industry which assisted in the construction of those great wooden sailing ships which figured so prominently in European history. Pitch making was a skilled trade, and many European surnames bear testimony to that fact today. In Polish, the word for pitch or tar is 'smola'. Any Polish telephone directory displays names such as Smola, Smolander, Smolen, Smolenski and Smolarz. These surnames simply mean 'the man who makes pitch'.

Likewise in Germany, the word for pitch is 'Teer', and it appears in names such as Teer and Teerman. Even the English have families whose name is Pitcher, Tarrier or Tarmen, to mention but a few. These all indicate that the trade of manufacturing pitch was extremely common throughout Europe.

So how did they make pitch before the growth of the petroleum and coal industries? Their first step was to obtain resin from the pine trees which at that time grew in dense forests throughout Europe. A herringbone pattern of cuts was gouged into the tree trunk and as the resin ran down the grooves it was collected in a pot at the base of the tree. Pine resin is still collected in this way in Poland, the Ukraine, Russia, Finland and other European countries where pine forests are still to be found.

When the resin had finished flowing, the trees were chopped down, covered in soil or ash, and burned slowly to produce a lightweight black pure form of carbon called charcoal. The last step in the process of making pitch was to add the powdered charcoal to the boiling pine resins. Different proportions of charcoal would produce pitch of different properties. It was this pitch which was used to waterproof the large ocean-going wooden ships. In my opinion, it is no coincidence that pitch today can be extracted from coal, much of which in Australia shows evidence of having been formed from pine tree debris.

Now, while I cannot say for sure that Noah obtained pitch for the ark exactly in this fashion, it does illustrate that you don't have to be able to extract either oil or coal from the ground in order to make pitch. Anyone who had cut down as many trees as Noah and his helpers for the manufacture of an ocean-going ark would certainly have found out about tree resins. If Europeans had a well-known and widely used method of making pitch before the discovery of petroleum, obviously Noah could also have had the same satisfactory way of waterproofing the ark with its covering of pitch. ■

archaeopteryx

■ **Carl Wieland**

CREATION SCIENTISTS and speakers have a wealth of documentation to support their claim that the general nature of the fossil record is hostile to evolution but supports the predictions of the creation model. All higher kinds of plants and animals appear abruptly and without transition. Are we misrepresenting evolution to insist on transitional forms? How many should we expect?

If we examine the mutation/selection theory, which is the mechanism of evolution held by the overwhelming majority today, we see that each change is slow and gradual, involving the accumulation of a vast number of small genetic coping mistakes, i.e. 'micromutations' or 'point mutations'. We see then, that the number of transitional forms involved in the transformation of, say, fish to amphibian over hundreds of millions of years would be incredibly vast (or 'innumerable' as Darwin predicted[1])—so much so that we would not expect to be able to recognize end forms and transitional forms separately—there would be an almost imperceptible 'oozing' of one kind into another.

Furthermore, it is an integral part of the theory that each form is successful, that is, each 'successive approximation' has a survival or reproductive advantage over its predecessor, or else it would not become established and give rise to subsequent forms. Therefore there is no reason whatever for the 'end forms' to have more chance of fossilization than the 'intermediates'. Sampling errors (which includes the 'poverty of the record' argument that Darwin invoked) are random, and while they could account for occasional or sporadic gaps, they may *not* be used as an excuse for *systematic* gaps.

What do most evolutionists offer in the place of the millions upon millions of transitional forms between higher kinds predicted by their model? The answer is usually a handful of transitional forms, and probably the most prominent is *Archaeopteryx*. You see, by making the prediction of *no* transitional forms versus *billions* of such forms, creationists are really 'laying it on the line'. All the evolutionist has to do is produce one indisputable transitional form between the higher kinds to seriously challenge the creation model. Others are occasionally mentioned, such as *Seymouria*, but these are not seriously considered as links by informed evolutionists (although many still do) for the simple reason that their supposed descendants appear 'earlier' in the fossil record than these 'transitional forms'! However, *Archaeopteryx* is usually proudly mentioned as a classical example of a transitional form (without of course mentioning that it is one of a handful compared to the millions Darwin hoped for).

Let's take a close look at this remarkable ancient creature. The first specimen was found in Upper Jurassic limestone in Bavaria in 1861, missing only the right foot, the lower jaw and a few cervical vertebrae. The second specimen was found ten miles away in 1877. There have been several more finds since, very fragmentary, but all our knowledge is based on these first two.

Archaeopteryx had many features which caused most investigators to class it immediately as a bird, *Aves*. The feathers

> *"Archaeopteryx stands alone, uniquely himself with no fossil between himself and either birds or reptiles"*

were identical in structure and arrangement to those of modern birds, a highly complex arrangement. It also had a bird-like posture, perching feet, a long sinuous neck holding its head high and a beaklike structure. However, it had many features not typical of modern birds and more typical of the class *Reptilia*. The most obvious two are the long, drooping tail and the teeth it possessed. Modern birds do not have teeth. However, extinct birds such as *Ichthyornis* and *Hesperornis*, which were unquestionably 100% birds, also had teeth. Closer examination reveals many other features which *Archaeopteryx* shared in common with reptiles. For example, the skull has many 'reptilian' features including lack of the posterior domelike expansion typical of birds otherwise.

Other such features are listed below and most may be visualized by a comparison diagram between *Archaeopteryx* and the modern pigeon.

- The cervical vertebrae lacked the heterocoelous centra peculiar to birds (heterocoelous means 'saddle shaped'; centra, singular centrum, are the central parts of vertebrae).
- The trunk vertebrae were not fused together as in birds.
- The weight of most birds is supported by a solid synsacrum, an extended bone at the end of the spine formed from several vertebrae fused together. *Archaeopteryx* had a tail which functioned to counterbalance his weight and the weight of his abdominal viscera was supported by a belly wall stiffened with gastralia, thin slivers of bone.
- The ribs were not connected by uncinate processes (hook-shaped protrusions) nor anchored into the sternum, as in birds.
- The pelvic bones were much smaller than most birds and did not extend nearly so far along the vertebral column. However, they had the avian backward twist of the pubes below the ischia.
- It had claws at the ends of the three digits. There are three living birds today which have claws in either the adult or juvenile form. *Arc haeopteryx* seems to have been able to crawl agilely through the trees as well as making short flights. That it was not a powerful flier may be inferred from the small area of origin which it had for flight muscles.
- The hand and wrist were not in the form of an inflexible blade.
- It had three independent metatarsals, rather than one as birds do.
- The fibula was equal in length to the tibia, as in reptiles, but not birds.

In summary, it may be said that *Archaeopteryx* is truly unique, and appears to exhibit a *mosaic* of characters, sharing some in common with the class *Aves* and some with the class *Reptilia*. It seems to have been suited to a lifestyle of short flights and agile crawling in trees, and those features which make it unquestionably a bird for classification purposes are uniquely and completely present and perfect. The feathers are not halfway transition from scales to feathers, an assumed transformation of the most astounding complexity. If for no other reason, this would disqualify it as a transitional form. A bat is not a transitional form between bird and land mammal, nor is a platypus transitional between duck and mammal, even though it exhibits some features of both.

The French theistic evolutionist and leading biophysicist Lecomte du Noüy (1883–1947) recognizes this:

> … we are not even authorized to consider the exceptional case of *Archaeopteryx* as a true link. By link, we mean a necessary stage of transition between classes such as reptiles and birds, or between smaller groups. An animal displaying characters belonging to two different groups cannot be treated as a true link as long as the intermediary stages have not been found, and as long as the mechanism of transition remains unknown.[2]

Furthermore, *Archaeopteryx* stands alone, uniquely himself with no fossil between himself and either birds or reptiles. Vertebrate paleontologist Barbara Stahl (1934–2014) writes:

> Since *Archaeopteryx* occupies an isolated position in the fossil record, it is impossible to tell whether the animal gave rise to more advanced fliers or represented only a side branch from the main line.[3] (This section of her book was reviewed by Prof. Alfred Romer.)

Scottish paleontologist William Swinton (1900–1994) states:

> The origin of birds is largely a matter of deduction. There is no fossil of the stages through which the remarkable change from reptile to bird was achieved.[4]

All of this is surely enough to establish that this bird is not a transitional form. Yet the above has been known for years, and still many evolutionists present it as a striking example of a transitional form. There has been a new discovery which surely demolishes the last hope in this direction. A bird which is unquestionably a true bird has been found which dates (by the evolutionists' own methods) at some 60 million years *older* than *Archaeopteryx*, which was 'dated' at about 150 million years old.[5] The find was assessed as above by paleontologist James Alvin Jensen (1918–1998) of Brigham Young University. The article also quotes noted dinosaur expert John Ostrom (1928–2005) of Yale:

> … we must now look for the ancestors of flying birds in a period of time much older than that in which *Archaeopteryx* lived.

As leading creationist Duane Gish (1921–2013) has said in another context, children cannot be older than their parents!

Unlike the evolutionary reconstructions shown on these two pages, Archaeopteryx was a true flying bird and not a transitional form

I will restate simply the reasons why *Archaeopteryx* cannot be regarded as a transitional form.

1. It has a 'mosaic' of characters in common with both groups but shows no true transitional structure such as a part-scale, part-feather.

2. There are no fossil links between it and either reptiles or birds—it stands alone.

3. True birds have been found which are assigned by evolutionists to an earlier time than *Archaeopteryx*. ■

References and notes

1. Darwin, C.R., *On the origin of species by means of natural selection, or the preservation of favoured races in the struggle for life*, Ch. 6, "On the absence or rarity of transitional varieties", 1st Edn, John Murray, 1859.
2. du Nouÿ, P.L. *Human Destiny*, Longmans, Green and Co., 1947.
3. Stahl, B.J., p. *Vertebrate History: Problems in Evolution* (McGraw–Hill 1973). In a later Dover edition (1985), she added: "retrieval of true bird fossils of Lower Cretaceous age has only strengthened the argument that the famous feathered *Archaeopteryx* may be an archaic side branch of the ancestral avian stock."
4. Swinton, W.E., The origin of birds; in: Marshall, A.J., ed., *Biology and Comparative Physiology of Birds*, p. 1, Academic Press, NY/London, 1960.
5. *Science-News* **112**:198, Sep. 1977.

This classic article from the very first issue showed the state of play 40 years ago. It's remarkable how this article has stood the test of time. More recent work strengthens the points still further,[1] and shows *Archaeopteryx* was a bird—not a missing link, and not a forgery either as some more recent critics asserted.

For example, *Archaeopteryx* had elliptical wings like modern woodland birds and fully-formed flying feathers (including asymmetric vanes and ventral, reinforcing furrows as in modern flying birds, and its claw geometry was suited for perching.[2]

Its skeleton had pneumatized vertebrae and pelvis, which indicate the presence of air sacs. This shows that they had the unique avian lung with one-way air flow, not the reptilian bellows lung.[3]

Analysis of *Archaeopteryx's* skull with computer tomography (CT) scanning shows that it had a brain like a modern bird's, three times the size of that of a dinosaur of equivalent size. This included large optic lobes for processing visual input, and inner ear structures (cochlea and semicircular canals) in the size range of modern birds, meaning good hearing and balance. Both would have been useful for flying. [4]

Furthermore, although a number of claimed 'feathered dinosaurs' have been discovered since this article, nearly all are 'dated' as millions of years *younger* than *Archaeopteryx* that is alleged to have descended *from* them. Indeed, they are not even older than the beaked and tailless bird *Confuciusornis* (120–125 million years), which evolutionists must regard as even more evolved.

1. See summary article, Sarfati, J. and Carter, R., Did dinosaurs evolve into birds? creation.com/dinosaur-bird-evolution, 16 April 2015.
2. Feduccia, A., Evidence from claw geometry indicating arboreal habits of Archaeopteryx, Science **259**(5096):790–793, 5 February 1993.
3. Christiansen, P. and Bonde, N., Axial and appendicular pneumaticity in Archaeopteryx, Proc. Royal Soc. London, Series B. 267:2501–2505, 2000.
4. Alonso, P.D., Milner, A.C., Ketcham, R.A., Cokson, M.J and Rowe, T.B., The avian nature of the brain and inner ear of Archaeopteryx, Nature **430**(7000):666–669, 5 August 2004; Witmer, L.M, Inside the oldest bird brain, perspective, same issue, pp. 619–620.

EX NIHILO

CREATION SCIENCE ASSOCIATION

Growing Pains cast in 1985

FROM
ATHEIST
TO
CHRISTIAN

SCOTT GILLIS interviews actor, producer, and Christian, **KIRK CAMERON**.

I first met Kirk while flying to upstate New York for a CMI speaking tour. I offered my seat to a young man so that he could sit next to his brother, and later learned that the siblings were sons of Kirk Cameron, who was on the plane with his family. They had just finished a week in Georgia at *Camp Firefly*, a charity founded by Kirk and his wife, Chelsea, 20 years earlier, to provide a much-needed week-long fun-filled vacation for terminally and seriously ill children and their struggling families. I had the privilege of speaking to Kirk about his life and family, and what it's like to be the rare combination of a Hollywood celebrity and a Christian.

THE ATHEIST

"I grew up in a family where we never went to church and God was not spoken of; He was never part of the conversation", Kirk said, adding, "Science was one of my favorite subjects. I loved cosmology, biology, anthropology." Like most people, Kirk was taught that evolution is an immutable scientific fact. "My science teacher had a very charismatic, dynamic personality. And he would laugh at the idea that there was some mystical voodoo power in the sky ... we were simply evolved and science knew how it all happened," Kirk said. "We were taught that there were people far more intelligent than we were, as 8th, 9th and 10th grade students, that understood these things, and God was just a fairytale—so that's what I believed."

Most young people want to be seen as rational, and this was no different for young Kirk. "I wanted to be counted among the intellectuals, and those who reasoned through things based on the evidence and facts." As is the case with the majority who are taught that evolution is the only rational scientific paradigm, any reasonable consideration of a divine Creator was logically excluded. Kirk quipped, "I believed God was part of a different trinity: the other two were Santa Claus and the Easter Bunny."

He had a few friends in school who believed in God, had some friendly debates with them, and went to church once or twice. Despite this, Kirk said, "I had some significant hurdles to overcome, and they were primarily rooted in my evolutionary atheistic beliefs. Like, we evolved, didn't we? Scientists have proven that."

> "I found out that creationists have intellect in spades on their side"

So how would an upcoming celebrity and self-described atheist come to know Christ?

At 17 years old, Kirk found himself right in the middle of the phenomenal success of *Growing Pains*. He described one of the main reasons he didn't believe in God: "It was the appeal of doing what I wanted. I was a celebrity. I had money, insane popularity, nobody said, 'No' to me, it was always, 'Yes, sir.' So it didn't make sense to consider a higher authority over me."

But even though he rejected God, he still had questions. "I was crushed in the middle of a very adult world and asking a lot of adult-sized questions, like, 'What happens when you die?' 'What's the meaning of life?' 'Is it to make as much money and have as much fun as you can?' I was beating most people in those last two categories and yet I sensed there's got to be something more meaningful than all that."

EXPOSED TO THE CREATOR

"God wasn't even a consideration, until I was in high school, when I met someone who took me to church." There, Kirk heard a message that was very new to him. The pastor told Kirk, "There are answers from the Bible. We didn't get here by some accident. You and I were not the unintended result of a process of time and chance that never had us in mind. In fact, we were created by an all-powerful, wise, loving, and just God; and our lives have purpose and meaning. In fact, there is a cosmic drama being played out between good and evil, and God wins."

That was a life-changing moment: "The chink in the armour was that there are a lot of really smart people who believed in God and who were Christians. I found out that creationists have intellect in spades on their side. That opened the door for me to the claim that there is a God."

Kirk began to really investigate Christianity, and as a consequence, soon after submitted his life to Christ.

For years now, Kirk has been well-known as an outspoken evangelist and apologist for the Christian faith. His experience as a former atheist helps him understand and relate to others who still do not believe. I asked Kirk what strategies he uses when sharing his faith with unbelievers who still believe evolution is an undisputed scientific fact. "Atheists will tell you that evolution really explains everything," Kirk said. He uses analogies to help explain how we can tell there is a Designer. "When you look at a painting, how do you know there's a painter when you can't see him, touch him, feel him or speak to him? Paintings don't paint themselves. Those things usually register with most people."

ADVICE WHEN CHALLENGED IN PUBLIC

Kirk is a celebrity who openly lives his Christian faith in the public eye, and this often results in public confrontations that turn into headlines. I asked Kirk what principles he uses to respond to these challenges in a biblical manner. "I tend to stick to the principle of speaking the truth in love. I fall back on sincerity all the time," Kirk said. "Your personal testimony often speaks volumes. It's my faith in the Word of God and the faithfulness of God that resulted in me being married to the same woman for 25 years, which is something like 250 in 'Hollywood years,' and living like we do with six kids, and being able to work on things that I'm passionate about."

When asked what advice he might give believers on standing boldly for their faith when challenged in public, Kirk responded, "It's very difficult to stand if you don't have something solid that you are standing on. So I would say, first of all, be sure you are standing on the truth. That's the only solid ground to argue from, when you know something is genuinely and sincerely true." Kirk added, "The most meaningful purpose of apologetics is to strengthen the believer. If you are arguing based on your feelings or hopes and wishes, people are going to push you over. So get your own questions answered for yourself first.

"Second, make sure you have a life that backs up what you say. Don't be a religious showoff or some sort of a hypocrite whose life speaks more loudly than your words and undermines everything you say. You'll know a tree by its fruit.

"Third, don't allow others to push you into a trap. Learn to discuss these things by honing the argument and directing the narrative yourself." Kirk gave an example by adding, "When someone says to me, 'Kirk, when did you stop believing in reason and start believing in God?' I will immediately say, 'That's the wrong question. What actually happened was that I blindly

believed that nothing created everything, which is illogical. Then I started looking at the facts, and reasoned through them and came to the obvious conclusion that God made all of this.'"

KNOW WHAT AND WHY YOU BELIEVE

"Being able to know what you believe and to know why you believe is critically important. And we need to have intellectual integrity, to know we are standing on solid ground." However, Kirk was quick to add, "Not everybody needs to have all the answers at the tip of their fingers, but we must have a basis of understanding that there are answers. I often find them through ministries like yours."

We must remember that there are so many who, like Kirk, need to be told about the 'chinks in the armour' of evolution, *and* the truth of the life-giving Gospel. Who around you needs to hear? Who around you might be like Kirk Cameron once was, needing someone to share the truth of the Bible with them? Perhaps we can take a page from Kirk's life, and be ready to share the truth of Scripture, remembering the words of 1 Peter 3:15, which commands us to be "… prepared to make a defense to anyone who asks you for a reason for the hope that is in you; yet do it with gentleness and respect." ∎

SCOTT GILLIS, B.A. Oregon State U.
Scott served in ministry for over 25 years as a youth pastor, teacher and a key leader in a church plant. He was the senior executive for a large construction firm before coming to work for CMI-US as the Chief Operations Officer. For more: creation.com/gillis.

> " ... being married to the same woman for 25 years ... is something like 250 in 'Hollywood years,' "

Article from
Creation 39(1):16–18
January 2017

The
BABY-
KILLERS

Update
Science since this article has both affirmed the reality of a human being from conception, while pro-abortionists are hardening even further against this human being in the womb, and sometimes even those newly outside the womb. See the articles in creation.com/humanlife.

Sebastian Kaulitzki /123RF

Editorial

Robert Doolan

NAOMI WOLF, the high-profile 32-year-old feminist author and Rhodes scholar, recently admitted that her morning sickness—and her seeing the baby inside moving on a scan—has helped her change her mind about abortion.

With her first baby due soon, Wolf said that she now rejects the abortion lobby's claim that a fetus isn't a human life but is merely a mass of tissue.

While she hasn't gone so far as to oppose abortion 'at all costs', Wolf is firing some heavy verbal artillery at her fellow feminists, whom she accuses of self-delusion, hardness of heart, and even lying when they say a death doesn't take place in abortion.

Amazingly, at the time Naomi Wolf's change of heart was taking place, an even bigger defection from the pro-abortion ranks was occurring.

Norma McCorvey, who under the pseudonym of 'Jane Roe' in 1973 prompted the landmark United States Supreme Court case *Roe vs Wade* (which decided in favour of abortion), announced in August that she now believes abortion is wrong. She has become a born-again Christian. Like Wolf, 47-year-old McCorvey is still working through some of the issues, but she has left her job at a Dallas abortion clinic to work for the pro-life group Operation Rescue, revealing that she had been haunted by the sight of empty swings in a playground.

In a further heart-wrenching disclosure, distinguished Australian novelist Peter Carey, 47, revealed in October that he deeply grieves over his dead children. His first child was aborted in 1961, then three more children died at birth. At his twins' cremation, Carey refused to give them any names, saying, "I don't believe in God".

He now says he regrets that decision. Although his children did not get to experience life outside their mother's womb, atheist Peter Carey knows they were human lives—his own children, not life-less fetal tissue or a cosmetically inconvenient biological condition.

Willful abortion is the willful taking of life. Abortion kills real babies. There is simply no convincing argument against this. A human fetus does not suddenly become human the moment it emerges from the mother's womb. It is a growing, God-given, human life from the moment of conception (Psalm 139:13–16), clearly identifiable as a human at all stages of growth.

The Bible is not only the truth, it is the truth *to such a degree* that even a non-Christian like Naomi Wolf can say that lying is required to try to justify the taking of a human life through abortion.

Ironically, this increasing recognition that unborn babies are human—and thus have the same rights as babies who have been born—may, instead of reducing abortion, extend it to include killing babies after birth, unless our culture restores its creation foundation. Why?

A society which believes everything has made itself (evolved) will increasingly reject any idea of a Creator, which means there can be no such thing as absolute, eternal standards. So everything, including 'human rights', is just a matter of opinion. If it becomes clear that all the millions already aborted with the blessing of evolutionary humanist ethics were already human, why—in the absence of God-given absolutes—should it continue to be wrong to kill unwanted babies *after* birth?

If you think this is far-fetched, consider influential pro-abortionist Peter Singer, author of the entry on Ethics in *Encyclopaedia Britannica*. Singer admits that abortion extinguishes human life, but not only has he been quoted as saying that a human fetus has fewer rights than a laboratory animal, he has recently been perceived to be openly arguing for infanticide. In *The Courier-Mail* (Brisbane, Australia) of 10 October 1995, Professor Singer, a convinced evolutionist, approvingly cites pagan societies which have allowed routine infant killing, and says:

Why—in the absence of religious beliefs about being made in the image of God, or having an immortal soul—should mere membership of the species *Homo sapiens* be crucial to whether the life of a being may or may not be taken?

Convinced evolutionists like Singer won't accept that we are not evolved animals, and that we have a unique place in God's creation (Genesis 1:26). Genesis is the key to the whole abortion debate. ∎

ROBERT DOOLAN
was editor of Creation *magazine from 1987 to 1996. He now edits educational materials for students and school teachers in Australia.*

Article from
Creation **18**(1):4
December 1995

HOW DOES THE BIBLE TEACH 6,000 YEARS?

©iStockPhoto.com/Sean_Warrer

■ Lita Cosner

The Bible's history gives us the answer to the age of the earth

MANY PEOPLE write in and ask, "How do we know that the earth is 6,000 years old from the Bible?" Given that the chronogenealogies—genealogies where the age of the father at the time of the son's birth is given in an unbroken chain—end shortly after Noah, how do we get from ~1600 AM (*anno mundi* = 'year of the world') to today, which we would argue is about 6000 AM?

How precisely can we know the earth's age?

The precision by which we can know the timing of historical events or ages of things is constrained by the precision of the data we're given. The timing we're given in the chronogenealogies is accurate to within one year of the event. By this, I mean we can know that Adam was 130 years old when he fathered Seth,

but we don't know if he was 130 and 3 months, or just shy of 131, for example. This is true for all the ages. So when you add up the chronogenealogies, we know that the Flood happened in 1656, plus up to less than 10 years, because we have 10 numbers that have less than a year of uncertainty. If all of the numbers were recorded just shy of the next birthday (for instance, Adam was 130 and 11 months when he fathered Seth, Seth was 105 and 11 months when he fathered Enosh, and so on), the Flood could have been as late as 1665 AM. But clearly this sort of small-scale uncertainty won't give any comfort to people who want to add thousands of years to human history.

The Flood to the Patriarchs

There is an unbroken chronogenealogy from Shem to Abraham in Genesis 11, and we're given the information elsewhere in Genesis[1] to extend the chronology until the relocation of Israel to Egypt when Jacob was 130 years old. Going by these numbers, Jacob went to Egypt in 642 + less than 12 years after the Flood, or 2298 + less than 22 years AM. The

chronogenealogy ends here, with nearly 2,000 years to go until Christ.[2] How do we extend the timeline?

The Patriarchs to the Exodus

Exodus 12:40 says that Israel was in Egypt for 430 years. This harmonizes well with Genesis 9:13 where God tells Abram that his descendants will be enslaved and mistreated for 400 years (enslavement did not happen on their arrival in Egypt but some time after Joseph died, when their number became threatening). So the Exodus happened in 2728 + less than 23 years AM.

The Exodus to the Kings

We know that Israel wandered in the desert for 40 years, meaning that they entered the Promised Land in 2768 + less than 24 years AM. But here the chronology becomes a bit hazier for a while. This is because we don't know *exactly* how long the conquest took, or exactly how long it was before the judges started ruling Israel. We're told how long each judge ruled, and how long each period of peace lasted, but some of these clearly overlap, and some judges clearly only ruled part of Israel, while another judge was ruling another part.

But we have a clear statement in 1 Kings that allows us to continue a reliable chronology. 1 Kings 6:1 says "In the four hundred and eightieth year after the Israelites had come out of Egypt, in the fourth year of Solomon's reign over Israel, in the month of Ziv, the second month, he began to build the temple of the Lord."

So if we subtract 124 years (40 each for the wandering in the desert, Saul's reign, and David's reign, and 4 for the partial reign of Solomon), we get a period of about 356 years for the judges, which fits well with the numbers in Judges if we assume a few overlaps. So Solomon began to build the Temple in 3208 + less than 23 years AM. Notice that even though we're thousands of years into history at this point, the uncertainty about the dates is less than 25 years!

The Kings to the Exile

If we go by the reigns of the kings of Judah, without assuming any co-regencies, from the Temple to the Exile of Judah would have been 429.5 years + less than 21 years. But we know that there *were* co-regencies in Judah, partly by comparing the kings of Judah to the kings of Israel.[3] If we do that, we know that from the Temple to the Exile of Judah is actually around 345 years, at around 3553 AM. At this point, it's possible to say what the date would be in our terms—and when one adjusts for the differences in calendrical systems, the vast majority consensus is 586 bc. This would mean that 1 ad would be around

FATHER/EVENT 1	SON/EVENT 2	AGE/LENGTH OF TIME	RUNNING TOTAL	REFERENCE
Adam	Seth	130	130	Genesis 5
Seth	Enosh	105	235	Genesis 5
Enosh	Kenan	90	325	Genesis 5
Kenan	Mahalel	70	395	Genesis 5
Mahalel	Jared	65	460	Genesis 5
Jared	Enoch	162	622	Genesis 5
Enoch	Methuselah	65	687	Genesis 5
Methuselah	Lamech	187	874	Genesis 5
Lamech	Noah	182	1056	Genesis 5
Noah	Flood	600	1656	Genesis 7:11
Flood	Arphaxad	2	1658	Genesis 11
Arphaxad	Shelah	35	1693	Genesis 11
Shelah	Eber	30	1723	Genesis 11
Eber	Peleg	34	1757	Genesis 11
Peleg	Reu	30	1787	Genesis 11
Reu	Serug	32	1819	Genesis 11
Serug	Nahor	30	1849	Genesis 11
Nahor	Terah	29	1878	Genesis 11
Terah	Abram	130	2008	Genesis 11
Abraham	Isaac	100	2108	Genesis 21:5
Isaac	Jacob	60	2168	Genesis 25:26
Jacob	Egypt	130	2298	Genesis 47:9
Jacob in Egypt	Exodus	430	2728	Exodus 12:40
Exodus	Temple begun	480	3208	1 Kings 6:1
Temple	Exile	345	3553	

4150 AM, plus or minus less than 50 years, and today we would be around 6150 AM, plus or minus less than 50 years.

The Bible is history!

It's clear that from the very first verse of Genesis, the Bible is concerned with giving a factual account of how God has interacted with the earth. This means that it must give *historically accurate* details, as well as being theologically accurate. In fact, what we believe about God is based on historical claims, so if the history is inaccurate, then the theology must be as

well! One of the ways the biblical authors communicated that they were giving actual history is by recording lifespans, or measuring the amount of time between certain events.

We can be confident that God's Word is accurate in its historical details as well as in what it tells us about theology. ■

References and notes

1. Genesis 5 goes from Adam to Noah and his sons; Genesis 11:10ff goes from Shem to Abram; Genesis 21:5 states that Abraham was 100 when Isaac was born; Genesis 25:8 states that Isaac was 60 when Jacob and Esau were born, and Genesis 47:9 says that Jacob was 130 when he went to Egypt.

2. Some argue for gaps in the Genesis 5 and 11 genealogies. For the reasons to take them as unbroken genealogies, see Sarfati, J. Biblical chronogenealogies, *J. Creation* 17(3):14–18, December 2003, creation.com/chronogenealogies.

3. For more detail about the challenges of interpreting the chronology of the kings of Israel and Judah, see Kaiser W., *A History of Israel: From the Bronze Age Through the Jewish Wars* (Broadville & Holman: Nashville, TN, 1998), pp. 292–300.

WHAT ABOUT DIFFERENT DATES FOR CREATION?

Many people have come up with dates for creation, such as James Ussher (4004 BC), Johannes Kepler (3992 BC), Gerhard Hasel (4178 BC), and Isaac Newton (~4000 BC). Additionally, there are various chronologies competing with each other today (though all with the same ballpark outcome) which would be more precise than this article, but also rely on assumptions that must come from a particular interpretation of the text. It is not the purpose of this article to choose any particular one of these chronologies, but rather to show how the plain interpretation of Scripture gives a straightforward chronology that leads us to believe the world is around 6,000 years old, regardless of which of these other chronological frameworks one uses.

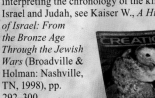

Article from
Creation **35**(1):54–55
January 2013

David Catchpoole

LOGGERHEAD TURTLES, thus termed because of their massive heads with large crushing jaws,[1] certainly get around. Just as the aptly-named 'Crush' in the animated movie *Finding Nemo* famously rode "the EAC" (East Australian Current), so real loggerheads migrate not just from north to south along the east coast of Australia[2] but also across the wide expanses of the Pacific and Atlantic oceans. For example, the journey that loggerhead turtles take from their nesting beaches in Japan to their feeding areas along the Californian coast and back is the longest migration known for a marine animal.[3] The enormous range of loggerhead turtles encompasses all but the most frigid waters of the world's oceans. How are loggerheads able to navigate across thousands of kilometres of open ocean, all the way back to the very beach where they hatched, to lay their eggs?

For over a decade now, it has been known that loggerheads, even as hatchlings, can use the earth's magnetic field to help them tell north from south and steer themselves along the right latitude.[4] How could

such an amazing ability have arisen by evolution? As famous evolutionist J.B.S. Haldane noted in 1949, evolution could never produce "various mechanisms such as the wheel and magnet, which would be useless till fairly perfect".[5] To detect the earth's magnetic field, loggerhead turtles must have some sort of magnetic sensor—thus, by Haldane's criterion, proving evolution false.[6]

Despite this, modern evolutionists have blithely continued to credit the loggerhead's navigational capabilities to evolution, illogically disregarding the sophisticated design required for magnetic field sensing. And now recent findings have caught evolutionists by surprise, as it

LES

at loggerheads with evolution

Newly hatched loggerheads are only about 5 cm (2 inches) long. They spend the first 7 to 12 years of their lives far out at sea, eventually returning to reproduce in the same area where they hatched.

Gary Bell/Oceanwidelmages.com

The shell on the back of the turtle is called the carapace, while the shell on the belly side is called the plastron. Loggerheads are the largest of all hard-shelled turtles (cf. leatherbacks which are bigger but have soft shells), with adult males generally reaching about 90 cm (3 ft) in shell length and weighing about 110 kg (250 lb). However, some reports say that larger specimens over 450 kg (1,000 lb) have been found!

has been discovered that loggerheads' positional and directional sense is way better than expected—explaining it without a Creator just got a whole lot harder.

Loggerhead longitude long-shot

Notwithstanding loggerhead turtles' ability to use magnetic cues to determine latitude, it was widely believed that this wasn't possible for longitude, because of how little the earth's magnetic field varies in the east-west direction around the globe. (When you travel north or south away from the earth's magnetic poles, their pull weakens substantially. In contrast, when travelling straight east or west, the intensity of the magnetic pull essentially doesn't change—only the *angle* of the magnetic pull changes, and that only to a very slight degree.) As Princeton University evolutionary biologist James L. Gould put it in 2008, regarding turtles and other migratory animals' uncanny ability to steer an accurate course: "A skeptic could reasonably believe that the latitudinal cue is magnetic, but that determining east-west position depends on magic."[7]

However, loggerheads have surprised evolutionists by demonstrating, "against reasonable expectation",[7] that the turtles can clearly determine longitude.[8,9] The researchers took turtles that had just hatched in Florida but had never been in the sea and put them in a pool surrounded by computer-controlled magnetic coil systems. The magnetic coils were set to reproduce the geomagnetic characteristics of two points on the loggerheads' trans-Atlantic migratory route at identical latitude—one in the western Atlantic, near Puerto Rico, and the other in the east, near the Cape Verde islands. Turtles in the 'Puerto Rico' tank swam northeast, just as loggerheads in the wild do when setting off on their migration, riding the currents that circle the Sargasso Sea and loop around the Atlantic. In the 'Cape Verde' pool however, the loggerhead hatchlings headed northwest, as if returning on the homeward leg of their circular migratory route.

So, loggerheads can detect *both* the intensity (field strength) and the inclination (angle) of the earth's magnetic field to create "a mental map that covers all four points of the compass".[10] Actually, it's more like a GPS[11] than a mere direction-finding compass. As University of North Carolina researcher Nathan Putman pointed out, "a compass doesn't really

Adult female loggerheads lay eggs in clutches of 100 to 150 eggs, burying them in dry sand. They do not hatch until about 60 days after being laid (during which time they might fall prey to wild pigs, raccoons, foxes or people—the eggs are very nutritious). After hatching underground, hatchlings dig their way up through the sand, waiting just beneath the surface until cooler temperatures signify nightfall. Then they pop out and scurry towards the ocean in a race against birds and other predators.

tell you where you are" whereas loggerheads' mental magnetic map "gives them positional information".[12] I.e., "turtles determine longitudinal position by using pairings of intensity and inclination angle as an X, Y coordinate system."

Putman adds that the findings might have a role to play in the development of human navigational technologies. "There may be situations where satellite might not be available, where this system of using two aspects of a magnetic field could be very useful," he said.[13]

In one sense, one can appreciate evolutionists' surprise at the loggerheads' "astounding migrational abilities"[10] in relation to longitude. After all, it took human navigators hundreds of years to figure out how to determine longitude in their long-distance voyages—even with the impetus of huge prizes offered by Spain, France and then Britain.[14] (Eventually, John Harrison (1693-1776) with his chronometers won the most money—£23,065, equivalent to over £3.3 million today.)

Thus the ability to determine longitude, requiring such intense and directed human intelligence, would surely not be found in the "tiny brains"[10] of loggerhead turtles—for surely such could not have arisen through evolutionary processes?

Indeed not—and therefore the fact that turtles *have* that capability points to its having originated from an intelligence *surpassing that of humans*, i.e. loggerheads have such features *by design*, not by evolution. In light of Romans 1:20 (those who deny the Creator are "without excuse"), one can see there's a *reason* that turtles are at loggerheads with evolution. They were created to *thwart* evolutionary storytelling!

And it's not just in relation to their design. There's no joy for evolutionists in the fossil record, either.

Turtle fossils 'all the way down'

As if there weren't already enough paleontological and other challenges posed by turtles to evolutionary theory,[15] the past decade has made it even more difficult to fit these singular creatures into an evolutionary 'tree'. Many and varied have been the century-long attempts to explain the origin and phylogenetic relationships (which presume a common ancestry of all living things) of turtles. Traditional ideas have been up-ended by more recent morphological and molecular studies.[16] But there is still no consensus—on the basis of comparisons of body form (morphology), evolutionists have variously claimed tuataras, lizards and snakes as turtles' closest relatives, but molecular comparisons draw other evolutionists to favour crocodiles and birds as the "living sister group" of turtles.[16]

The recent discovery of a turtle fossil in Upper Triassic strata in China, presumed by evolutionists to be 220 million years old,[17] has re-ignited another debate. Dubbed *Odontochelys semitestacea*, two reviewers (Tyler Lyson and Scott Gilbert) say the fossil "reopens the debate regarding the origin of the turtle shell".[18] This is the debate as to how the turtle's carapace might have arisen in an evolutionary stepwise process from other parts of the turtle body over long periods of time. But, as evolutionists have admitted, "the turtle body plan is quite unique among vertebrates and is difficult to derive from a generalized pattern of the amniotes."[19] (Amniotes = reptiles, birds, mammals.) And in the absence of definitive transitional fossils, such evolutionary speculation is exactly

that—speculation![20] Stasis is a feature of the turtle fossil record—turtles have always been turtles.[21] The title of the paper by Lyson and Gilbert summed up the evolutionary conflict perfectly, *Turtles all the way down: loggerheads at the root of the chelonian tree*. This sentence from their closing paragraph is just as candid:

> "The new discovery of the beautifully preserved fossil *O. semitestacea* produces more questions than it answers, reopening questions of turtle origins, shell evolution, and original paleoecology."[18]

You can find a *correct* answer, based on *true* history, to the question of the origin of turtles, and the timing of the fossilization of the *O. semitestacea* turtle fossil, in the Bible. Turtles were created on Day 5 of Creation Week (see box right) only about 6,000 years ago, and this fossil dates from the Flood of Noah's day, about 4,500 years ago—a hugely violent, worldwide event. That's why this and so many other fossils are, like it, "beautifully preserved".[18] But this explanation only works for those who don't want to "deliberately forget"—2 Peter 3:5–6. ■

References and notes

1. Chapter 10, "Loggerheads: A Crushing Jaw" in Spotila, J., *Sea Turtles: A complete guide to their biology, behavior and conservation*, The John Hopkins Community Press, USA, 2004.
2. Turtle's Finding Nemo journey, *The Daily Telegraph*, www.dailytelegraph.com.au, 27 April 2008.
3. Lohmann, C. and Lohmann, K., Sea turtles, *Current Biology* **16**(18):R784–R786, 2006.
4. Sarfati, J., Turtles—reading magnetic maps, *Creation* **21**(2):30, 1999; creation.com/turtlemap.

Article from
Creation 33(3):28–31
July 2011

5. *Is Evolution a Myth? A Debate between D. Dewar and L.M. Davies vs. J.B.S. Haldane*, Watts & Co. Ltd / Paternoster Press, London, 1949, p. 90.

6. And loggerheads, in company with all multicellular creatures, have an enzyme called ATP synthase, which is actually a rotary motor—a type of 'wheel' (see *Creation* 31(4):21–23, 2009; creation.com/atp-synthase), thus fulfilling Haldane's other criterion.

7. Keim, B., Navigational 'magic' of sea turtles explained, *Wired Science*, wired.com, 24 February 2011.

8. Pearson, A., Loggerhead turtles have a magnetic sense for longitude, *New Scientist*, newscientist.com, 25 February 2011.

9. Putman, N., Endres, C., Lohmann, C., and Lohmann, K., Longitude perception and bicoordinate magnetic maps in sea turtles, *Current Biology* 21(4),

doi:10.1016/j.cub.2011.01.057, March 2011.

10. Macrae, F., No need to shell out for a satnav: Loggerhead turtles use Earth's magnetic field to make a mental map of their migration, dailymail.co.uk, 24 February 2011.

11. Global Positioning System; see also interview with satellite specialist Dr Mark Harwood, *Creation* 26(4):18–23, 2004; creation.com/what-goes-up.

12. Palca, J., For turtles, Earth's magnetism is a built-in GPS, *NPR News*, wap.npr.org, 2 March 2011.

13. Sea turtles' migration mystery is 'solved', *BBC News*, bbc.co.uk, 25 February 2011.

14. Gould, J., Animal navigation: The longitude problem, *Current Biology* 18(5): R214–R216, 2008.

15. Weston, P., Turtles, *Creation* 21(2):28–31, 1999; creation.com/turtles.

16. Zardoya, R. and Meyer, A., The evolutionary position of turtles revised, *Naturwissenschaften* 88:193–200, 2001.

17. Li, C. and 4 others, An ancestral turtle from the Late Triassic of southwestern China, *Nature* 456:497–501, 2008.

18. Lyson, T. and Gilbert, S., Turtles all the way down: loggerheads at the root of the chelonian tree, *Evolution & Development* 11(2):133–135, 2009.

19. Kuratani, S., Kuraku, S. and Nagashima, H., Evolutionary developmental perspective for the origin of turtles: the folding theory for the shell based on the developmental nature of the carapacial ridge, *Evolution & Development* 13(1):1–14, 2011.

20. The *Odontochelys semitestacea* fossil and the evolutionary controversy arising are discussed in detail in Sarfati, J., *The Greatest Hoax on Earth—Refuting Dawkins on evolution*, CBP, USA, pp. 141–143. (Available via creation.com/s/10-2-555.)

21. Living fossil' turtle evidence—no evolution, Ref. 15, p. 29; Bell, P., Evolutionary Stasis: Double–Speak and Propaganda, *Creation* 28(2):38–40, 2006; creation.com/evolutionary-stasis.

DAVID CATCHPOOLE, B.Ag.Sc.(Hons.), Ph.D.
After working as a plant physiologist and science educator, Dr Catchpoole worked for many years as a scientist/speaker for Creation Ministries International *(Australia). He continues to write for CMI. For more: creation.com/catchpoole.*

Loggerhead turtles can use their powerful jaws to crush prey like conches, crabs and other animals with hard shells. But they also eat softer foods such as jellyfish, seaweed and a brown alga called sargassum.

Loggerheads are no landlubbers

Loggerhead turtles (*Caretta caretta*) live in oceans all over the world, except in the most frigid waters. Having paddle-like flippers for swimming, and streamlined carapaces, loggerheads are renowned for their long-distance oceanic migrations (up to 4,828 km),[1] and pin-point accurate navigation. (Adult females often exhibit natal beach nesting, i.e. laying their eggs on the very same beach where they themselves hatched.)

Despite their evident aquatic prowess, evolutionists say these sea turtles are "limited by their land-dwelling ancestry", as they must breathe air and nest on dry land.[2]

But a creationist perspective makes much more sense. Their need to breathe air is no impediment to them at all, being able to dive for up to 20 minutes, and even rest for hours without breathing. (In any case, loggerheads' food is mostly found in the relatively shallow coastal waters, where their average dive is only three to four minutes.) Their "attachment" to land during their lifetimes is minimal: no more than two months as eggs buried in sand, a few hours at most as hatchlings journeying from nest to sea, and a few hours again for adult females when making landfall to lay eggs. So loggerheads are best viewed as sea creatures, created on Day 5 of Creation Week.

But some might ask, how could sea turtles have survived the global Flood of Noah's day, with no dry land available for nesting, if they were not taken aboard the Ark? It's easy to understand in light of the fact that females only nest *every two to five years*. So, once the Flood waters went down, the surviving sea turtles could begin reproducing again. And as female loggerheads lay up to five clutches of eggs in one nesting season, with up to 150 eggs per clutch—that's a lot of turtles!—loggerhead populations could rapidly recover from Flood losses and from any interruptive effect of the Flood on reproductive cycles. Loggerheads attain mature size between 10 and 30 years of age, and reproductive life span after reaching maturity is estimated at about 32 years. So, no problem for loggerheads to survive the Flood.

References and notes

1. University of Michigan Museum of Zoology, *Caretta caretta*—loggerhead sea turtle, animaldiversity.ummz.umich.edu/site/accounts/information/Caretta_caretta.html, acc. 14 March 2011.

2. Lohmann, C. and Lohmann, K., Sea turtles, *Current Biology* 16(18):R784–R786, 2006.

Gary Bell/Oceanwideimages.com

IS *Jesus Christ* THE CREATOR GOD?

■ **Russell Grigg**

THE BIBLE affirms in several places that Jesus Christ is the Creator God. For example, "All things were made through him, and without him was not any thing made that was made" [the Word, in Greek ὁ λόγος (*ho logos*) = Jesus Christ]" (John 1:1–3), and "For by him [Jesus Christ] all things were created" (Colossians 1:16).

If this is true, then we should expect to see some parallelism between what happened at creation and the works of Jesus during his ministry on earth. What do we find?

First let us consider what kind of evidence we are looking for.

Some of the essential and distinctive elements of creation, as revealed in Genesis chapter l, as well as elsewhere in the Bible, are:

1. Creation involved the act of God in bringing into being immediately and instantaneously matter which did not previously exist, without the use of pre-existing materials or secondary causes; for example, in the creation of the heavens and the earth, as recorded in Genesis 1:1. Creation also involved the shaping, combining, or transforming of existing materials, as when God created Adam from the dust of the ground (Genesis 2:7), and Eve from Adam's rib (Genesis 2:21–22).

2. Creation involved the imparting of life to otherwise lifeless matter (Genesis 2:7).

3. The mechanism of creation, or the means whereby the above aspects were accomplished, was by the Word of the Lord, that is, God said (= God willed it to happen) … and it happened.

4. The purpose or motive of God in creating was to display His glory (Psalm 19:1), to make known His power, His wisdom, His will, and His holy name (Exodus 9:16), and that He might receive glory from His created beings (Revelation 4:11).

Note: We should not expect to find exact parallels between the miracles of Jesus and what happened at Creation, as Jesus did not come to re-create the universe, but "to seek and to save the lost" (Luke 19:10) and "to give his life as a ransom for many" (Matthew 20:28). With this in mind, let's compare these four aspects of creation with the works of Jesus.

1. Creation out of nothing and/or from existing materials

Several of Jesus' miracles involved the creation of new material. Whether this was out of nothing or from existing materials is not spelt out by the Gospel writers, as they major on the fact of the miracles and the effects they produced (John emphasizes the teaching that Jesus drew from them), rather than on any analyses of the *modus operandi*.

Jesus' first *miraculous sign to His disciples* involved the creation of wine (His first *miracle* recorded in the Gospels is actually the creation of the universe (John 1:3), as mentioned above). At a wedding breakfast, Jesus instructed the waiters to fill six stone water-pots with water, and then to take them to the master of ceremonies of the wedding banquet.

When they arrived, the water had been turned into wine (John 2:1–11), that is, there had been the instantaneous creation of the carbon atoms and chemical molecules that made up the grape sugar, carbon dioxide, colouring matter, etc., of the wine.

Other examples are the two times when Jesus fed a multitude: on the first occasion more than 5,000 people from five loaves and two fish—recorded in all four Gospels—and on the second occasion more than 4,000 people from seven loaves and a few little fish (Matthew 15:32–38).

Here there were bread and fish to begin with on both occasions. Jesus either caused these original items to multiply, or He may have dispensed all the original food and then created new loaves and fishes until everyone was fed. Either way, Jesus created sufficient extra bread and fish, not only to feed many thousands of people, but also to provide 12 basketfuls of leftovers on the first occasion and seven basketfuls of leftovers on the second. This involved not just the creation of the appropriate carbohydrate, protein and other molecules, but their immediate arrangement into the complex forms and structures needed to make baked bread and fish (albeit dead and cooked).

Some of Jesus' miracles of healing, for example, of lepers (Luke 5:12–13; 17:11–19), the blind (Matthew 9:27–30), and paralytics (Luke 5:17–6:10), involved the instant repair of tissues, nerves, muscles, etc., and the instantaneous growth or regrowth of healthy cells. The net result was the creation of healthy functioning parts of the body to replace diseased, non-functioning or atrophied parts.

2. The giving of life

Jesus gave life to the dead on three occasions: to a widow's son (Luke 7:11–16), to Jairus' daughter (Luke 8:41–55), and to his friend Lazarus (John 11:1–44).

In the case of Lazarus, the body had been in the grave for four days, and his sister Martha said, "Lord, by this time there will be an odor, for he has been dead four days" (John 11:39). This shows that the process of decomposition whereby a dead body eventually becomes dust had already begun. So here we have a parallel with what happened on the sixth day of creation when God formed Adam from the dust of the ground and breathed into his nostrils the breath of life, and Adam became a living being (Genesis 2:7). Jesus called Lazarus back to life, and the molecules of matter that were in the process of becoming dust became, again, a living human being.

In the case of the widow's son and of Jairus' daughter, death was more recent, that is, probably on the same day that Jesus gave life to their dead bodies. The principle still applies.

3. The method Jesus used

Jesus appeared to use a variety of means in performing His miracles. These included touching lepers, the blind, and the deaf; the use of saliva to heal a deaf mute (Mark 7:31–35) and a blind man (Mark 8:22–25);

Then he told them, "Now draw some out and take it to the master of the banquet."

John 2:8

Article from
Creation **13**(3):43–45
June 1991

... *Jesus called in a loud voice, "Lazarus, come out!"*

John 11:43

the use of clay (with instructions to wash) to heal a blind man (John 9:1–41); and the word of command to heal, to raise the dead, and to exorcise demons.

However, what happened in these and in all of Jesus' miracles was that Jesus willed the event to happen and it did. This is nowhere better illustrated than in the healing of the nobleman's son. Jesus was at Cana in Galilee and a certain royal official asked Him to travel to Capernaum to heal his son who was close to death. The Apostle John records what happened:

So he came again to Cana in Galilee, where he had made the water wine. And at Capernaum there was an official whose son was ill. When this man heard that Jesus had come from Judea to Galilee, he went to him and asked him to come down and heal his son, for he was at the point of death. So Jesus said to him, "Unless you see signs and wonders you will not believe." The official said to him, "Sir, come down before my child dies." Jesus said to him, "Go; your son will live." The man believed the word that Jesus spoke to

him and went on his way. As he was going down, his servants met him and told him that his son was recovering. So he asked them the hour when he began to get better, and they said to him, "Yesterday at the seventh hour the fever left him." The father knew that was the hour when Jesus had said to him, "Your son will live." And he himself believed, and all his household. This was now the second sign that Jesus did when he had come from Judea to Galilee. (John 4:46–53).

Capernaum was about 27 km (17 miles) from Cana as the crow flies, which means there was no way that the sick son, or anyone else in Capernaum, could have heard Jesus or been influenced by His physical presence in Cana.

Jesus willed the sick boy to recover, from 27 km away, and he did so. Similarly, Jesus willed the water to become wine, as it was being taken into the wedding feast in Cana, and it did so. He willed the bread and fish to form and they did, and He willed the 10 lepers to become well after they had left Him and were on

their way to the priests, and they were healed (Luke 17:11–19). It is interesting that a Gentile centurion recognized this authority of Jesus. The centurion had sent servants to request Jesus to come and heal his servant, as Luke records:

And Jesus went with them. When he was not far from the house, the centurion sent friends, saying to him, 'Lord, do not trouble yourself, for I am not worthy to have you come under my roof. Therefore I did not presume to come to you. But say the word, and let my servant be healed. For I too am a man set under authority, with soldiers under me: and I say to one, "'Go," and he goes; and to another, "Come," and he comes; and to my servant, "Do this," and he does it.' When Jesus heard these things, he marveled at him, and turning to the crowd that followed him, said, 'I tell you, not even in Israel have I found such faith.' And when those who had been sent returned to the house, they found the servant well. (Luke 7:6–10)

The centurion realized that his earthly commands would be obeyed instantly and without question. So how much more would the Creator's. He recognized that the voice of Jesus could not be heard by his sick servant, but the result, brought about by the exercise of Jesus' authority, would be no less effective because of this.

4. Jesus' glory seen in his miracles

After narrating Jesus' first miraculous sign to His disciples—the turning of water into wine—the Apostle John says, He "manifested his glory. And his disciples believed in him" (John 2:11). When Jesus heard that Lazarus was sick, He said, "This illness does not lead to death. It is for the glory of God, so that the Son of God may be glorified through it." And then, after Lazarus had died and before Jesus raised him to life, He said to Martha, "Did I not tell you that if you believed you would see the glory of God?" (John 11:4, 40).

John calls Jesus' miracles "signs" and in his Gospel John shows which way the signs point: "these are written so that you may believe that Jesus is the Christ, the Son of God, and that by believing you may have life in his name" (John 20:31).

Conclusion

Jesus Christ is the Creator God. Not only does Scripture affirm it, but during His earthly life and ministry He did the very things we would expect the Creator God to do. He did them in the way that we would expect the Creator God to do them—by His word of authority and the exercise of His will. And the doing of them displayed His glory.

This is a source of praise and inspiration for those who believe the Word of God, and at the same time it is a reproof of the doctrine of theistic evolution. The thought that Jesus might have used evolutionary chance random processes to heal the sick or give life to the dead is as unsustainable as the idea that He used such processes to create and give life to all things 'in the beginning'. ■

RUSSELL GRIGG, M.Sc.(Hons.)
was an industrial chemist before serving 20 years with Overseas Missionary Fellowship (now OMF International). He is a staff member of Creation Ministries International *in Australia. For more:* creation.com/grigg.

... "I am the resurrection and the life. The one who believes in me will live, even though they die; and whoever lives by believing in me will never die. Do you believe this?"

John 11:25-26

A COAT OF MANY

CAPTIVATING CHAMELEONS

Jonathan Sarfati

THE CHAMELEON (Greek: 'ground lion') is a lizard with many remarkable features. About 90 species have been identified,[1] and 59 of them live in Madagascar.[2] However, there are only two genera,[1] which probably means that there were originally only one or two created kinds, which now have many varieties.

They live mostly in trees and eat mainly insects, although large chameleons can eat birds. Most chameleons grow to 17–25 cm (7–10 inches) long, while the longest can reach 60 cm (2 ft). Chameleons are sometimes insulted as 'the most primitive group of lizards',[3] but they have many unique design features.

Colour change

Chameleons are famous for being able to change their colour. However, "It is a popular misconception that the chameleon changes its colour to match that of the background."[1] Rather, they have a basic pattern that provides camouflage, and the colour changes are due to heat, light, and can also reflect their mood! For example, if a panther chameleon gets angry, then red and yellow replace its normal colour.[4] Perhaps other chameleons recognize this as a warning to keep away? Many believe that the chameleon's colour helps to communicate its mood to other chameleons—'wearing its heart on its sleeve', so to speak. One type of male chameleon, when he wants to attract a female, will change from brown to purple and light blue, with his eyelids turning yellow with green spots.

How do they do it? They change colour with their highly structured skin. Underneath a transparent outer layer, there are two layers of red and yellow pigments, contained in cells called *chromatophores*. Below that are two more layers, one reflecting blue and another reflecting white. Deeper still is a layer of the dark brown pigment melanin contained in cells called *melanophores*.[5] These are the most important for colour change, because they have 'tentacles' reaching into the upper layers.

The colour changes when the cells expand or contract. E.g. a calm chameleon might look green when its yellow chromatophores are partly contracted, letting reflected blue light through as well. An angry chameleon may be yellow

COLOURS

because the yellow cells are large enough to block the blue light from shining through.[2] Yellow can also result when the blue layer is missing, allowing the white light from the next layer to shine through and brighten the other colours.

The skin lightens when the melanophores pull melanin inwards. But when a chameleon is enraged, the melanin spreads into the outer layers and the skin may blacken.

Telephoto lizards[6]

Chameleons have large eyes that can move independently. They also use a unique 'telephoto principle' to measure distances. Consider an old-style camera where you turn a dial to bring an object into focus—you could tell how far away the object is by reading the distance setting of the dial when the object is focused.[7]

For the chameleon to focus accurately, the lens must form a large image on the retina. The chameleon's eye produces the largest image of any vertebrate compared to its size. This is formed by an "astonishing"[7] negative lens,[8] likely "unique among animals",[7] i.e. it makes light diverge rather than converge.

The chameleon can see a sharp image of an object from almost any distance away. That is, its eye can accommodate very well, so it can even clearly see an object just 3 cm (just over an inch) away. In contrast, in human vision, objects become blurry if they are closer than twice that distance. We really need objects to be 30 cm (1 ft) away before we can see them as clearly as a chameleon can.

Terrific tongue

The chameleon needs this fine judgment of distance to capture prey with its tongue. This is another remarkable feature—the tongue can reach up to 1½ times the lizard's body length. The acceleration of this 'ballistic tongue' is amazing—50 g (i.e. 50 times the acceleration due to gravity), while astronauts and jet fighter pilots will pass out at only 10 g. The chameleon uses special supercontracting muscle, "unique among vertebrates" and otherwise found only in invertebrates.[9] This is necessary to produce the tension over the great changes in muscle length.

A special high-speed X-ray camera is required for scientists to film the tongue through its entire movement (including inside the mouth).[10]

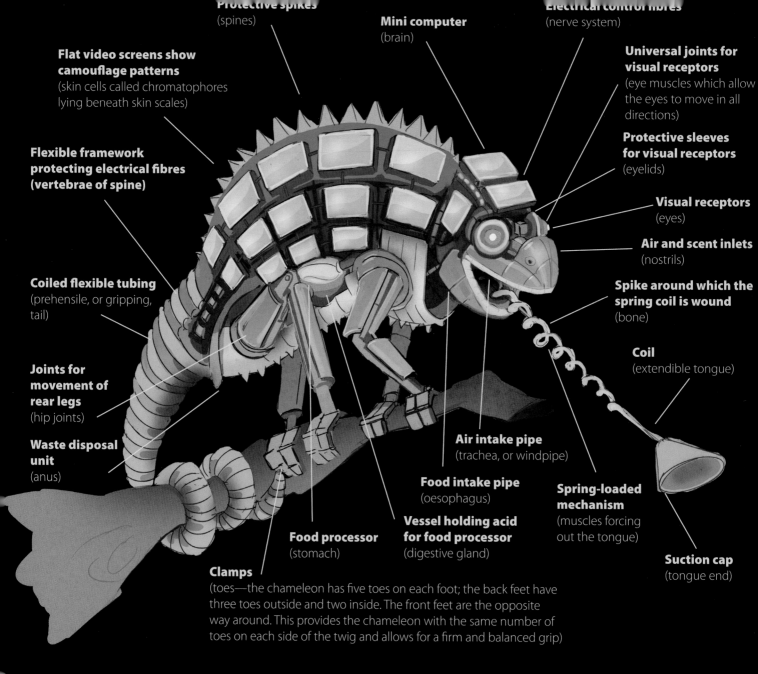

Suction cap

Most lizards catch insects on their tongue just by the stickiness of the moist surface. But the chameleon's fast tongue also manages to capture large, smooth prey. It does this with yet another mechanism. Just before the tongue hits the prey, two muscles pull the central part of the tip backwards, forming a suction cap.[3]

Catapult

How does the tongue accelerate so much? Even supercontractile muscle can't explain that totally—it would need to generate 10 times as much power as it does. Some animals generate high accelerations by using their legs as levers, but even a kangaroo rat can reach only 19 g while jumping.[11]

Close analysis reveals that the tongue has an ingenious catapult system.[12] A catapult is a machine with a stiff frame, allowing a large force to store energy in an elastic material, then releasing it suddenly to accelerate a small mass. An article in the journal *Science* said, "The chameleon's 'sliding spring' is remarkably compact, efficient and easy to control."[11] The lead researcher, Dr Johan van Leeuwen, of Wageningen University in the Netherlands, said, "So far we have not seen a parallel structure in biology or mechanics—it is a completely novel design."[13]

National Geographic said, "The collagen catapult is beginning to receive attention from engineers who believe it may have a variety of medical applications."[13]

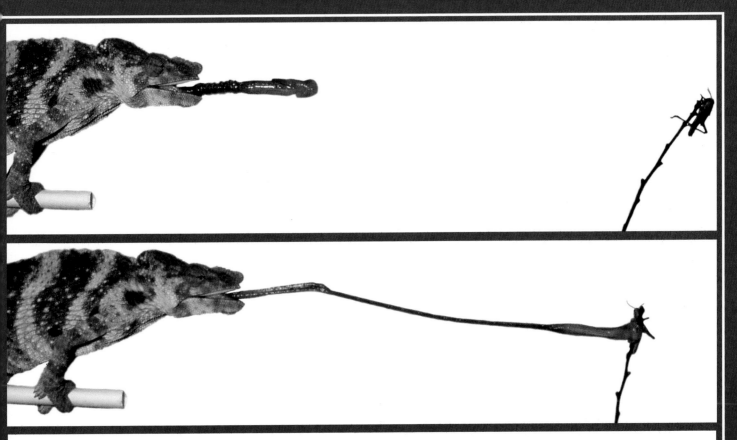

CHAMELEON CATAPULT

The chameleon tongue has a bone, which provides the stiff frame. Surrounding the bone are at least 10 slippery sheaths. These contain coiled collagen fibres, which are the elastic material. The sheaths, in turn, are surrounded by the powerful accelerator muscles, providing the stretching energy.

When the chameleon wants to flick out its tongue, it activates these muscles. Now muscle is incompressible, i.e. its volume remains the same. (For example, when you flex your biceps, the muscle contracts, and to keep the volume constant, it bulges outward.) In the chameleon tongue, the muscles squeeze inward, and to keep the volume constant they lengthen along the tongue. This stretches the sheaths like elastic bands.

When the sheaths come to the rounded tip of the tongue bone, they slide forward and off. With the bone out of the way, the sheaths can relax inward and contract in length quickly. This forces the tongue off the bone, and the 'sliding spring' mechanism releases the stored energy to shoot the tongue forward at dazzling speed. Then the concentric sheaths extend like tubes of a telescope.[1]

The tongue projector is more efficient than a man-made catapult—the latter loads and releases the energy along the same path, while the chameleon tongue releases the energy in a different path. This means that the tongue needs no extra moving parts to release the tension suddenly, because the energy is released as the tongue slips forward and off the bone. Also, while the acceleration is certainly sudden, the energy is still released steadily as the sheaths slide off in turn, rather than all at once. Otherwise a lot of the energy would be wasted in deforming the tongue, and be lost in vibrations.[2]

References and notes

1. Schilthuizen, M., Slip of the chameleon's tongue, *Science Now*, sciencenow. sciencemag.org, 8 March 2004.
2. Müller, U.K. and Kranenbarg, S., Power at the tip of the tongue, *Science* **304**(5668):217–219, 9 April 2004 | doi:10.1126/science.1097894.

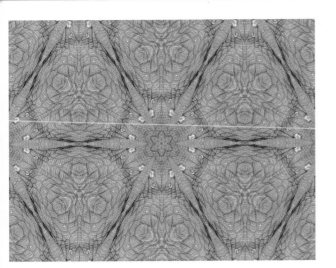

UPDATE: Iridophores produce iridescent colours.

Iridophores are arrays of microscopic crystals of guanine, a DNA base that can also form reflective crystals. This arrangement acts as a diffraction grating, splitting and spreading the light into the different colours of the spectrum, producing iridescent colours, as in blue butterflies. Furthermore, the chameleon can change colour quickly by adjusting the spacing between the crystals. When the chameleon is relaxed, the crystals are close together, reflecting short wavelengths of light, i.e. blue. If it is agitated, the lattice expands, spreading out the crystals, reflecting longer wavelengths, i.e. yellow and red.[1]

References and notes

1. Teyssier, J. *et al.*, Photonic crystals cause active colour change in chameleons, *Nature Communications* **6**(6368), 10 March 2015 | doi:10.1038/ncomms7368. See also Chameleon colour nanotechnology, *Creation* **37**(3):9, 2015.

Created, not evolved

One of the papers[3] on the tongue's design had a curious section, "Evolutionary considerations". The author admitted that the suction cap and the ballistic tongue are both essential to capture prey, i.e. one is useless without the other. Yet he interpreted this as evidence that they must have "evolved simultaneously

… early in their evolutionary history". A far better interpretation is that chameleons have always been chameleons, and were designed with both these mechanisms fully functional.

There is a good lesson here. *Practical* biological research assumes that features of living things have a function, so it makes sense to find out how they work. This makes perfect sense if these features have been designed for a purpose. So all the *useful* research was carried out as if the researchers were creationists for all practical purposes. But then evolutionists try to make up just-so stories to explain how these features evolved. Yet this extra "Evolutionary considerations" section added nothing whatever of practical value.[14]

So how does the chameleon's insect-eating fit with the biblical teaching of death as the result of the Fall of Adam? First, insects are probably not 'living' in the sense of being 'soulish', as vertebrates are—the Bible never calls them *nephesh chayyah* (living souls/creatures). Second, this could have been a latent feature programmed into the genes by the Creator who foreknew the Fall. ■

References and notes

1. Article 'chameleon', *Encyclopædia Britannica* **3**:69, 15th ed., 1992.
2. Raxworthy, C.J., A Truly Bizarre Lizard, *The Living Edens*, 20 April 2004.
3. Herrel, A., Meyers, J.J., Aerts, P. and Nishikawa, K.C., The mechanics of prey prehension in chameleons, *J. Experimental Biology* **203**:3255–3263, 2000.
4. *National Geographic Explorer*—Chameleons, magma.nationalgeographic.com, 21 April 2004.
5. Holladay, A., How do chameleons change color and how do they know what color to change to?, *Wonderquest*, wonderquest.com/chameleons.htm, 14 March 2001.
6. Telephoto lizard, Focus, *Creation* **19**(1):7, 1996.
7. Land, M., Fast-focus telephoto eye, *Nature* **373**(6516):658–659, 23 February 1995; comment on ref. 10.
8. Ott, M. and Schaeffel, F., A negatively powered lens in the chameleon, *Nature* **373**(6516):692–694, 23 February 1995.
9. Herrel, A., Meyers, J.J., Timmermans, J.P. and Nishikawa, K.C., Supercontracting muscle: producing tension over extreme muscle lengths, *J. Experimental Biology* **205**:2167–2173, 2002.
10. Snelderwaard, P.Ch., de Groot, J.H. and Deban, S.M., Digital video combined with conventional radiography creates an excellent high-speed X-ray video system, *J. Biomechanics* **35**:1007–1009, 2002.
11. Müller, U.K. and Kranenbarg, S., Power at the tip of the tongue, *Science* **304**(5668):217–219, 9 April 2004.
12. de Groot, J.H. and van Leeuwen, J.L., Evidence for an elastic projection mechanism in the chameleon tongue, *Proc. Royal Society London B*, **271**(1540):761–770, 7 April 2004.
13. Trivedi, B.P., 'Catapults' give chameleon tongues superspeed, study says, 19 May 2004.
14. See also Wieland, C., Evolution and practical science, *Creation* **20**(4):4, 1998.

JONATHAN SARFATI, B.Sc.(Hons.), Ph.D., F.M.

Dr Sarfati's Ph.D. in physical chemistry is from Victoria University, Wellington, NZ. He is the author of some of the world's best-known creation books. A former NZ chess champion, he works for Creation Ministries International *(in Australia 1996–2010, thereafter in Atlanta, USA). For more: creation.com/sarfati.*

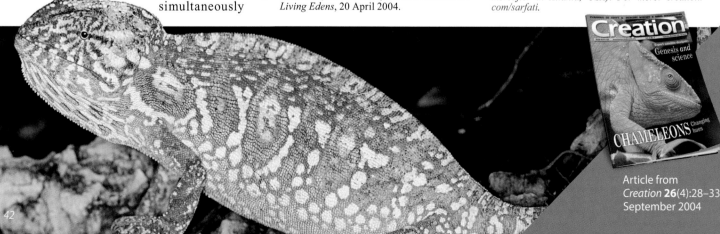

Article from *Creation* **26**(4):28–33 September 2004

THE MYTH OF 1%

Human and chimp DNA *are very different*

■ **Don Batten**

WE STILL commonly see statements that human and chimp DNA are 'almost identical', with only 1% difference claimed. For example, in a 2012 report on the sequencing of the other chimpanzee species, the bonobo:

"Ever since researchers sequenced the chimp genome in 2005, they have known that humans share about 99% of our DNA with chimpanzees, making them our closest living relatives."[1]

And this was not from some disreputable source, but from the publishers of *Science*, published by the American Association for the Advancement of Science. *Science* is considered one of the top two science journals in the world (the other is *Nature* from the UK).

The original 1% claim goes back to 1975.[2] This was a long time before a direct comparison of the individual 'letters' (base pairs) of human and chimp DNA was possible—the first draft of the human DNA was not published until 2001 and for the chimp it was 2005. The 1975 figure came from crude comparisons of very limited stretches of human and chimp DNA that had been pre-selected for similarity. The chimp and human DNA strands were then checked for how much they stuck to each other—a method called DNA hybridization.

Would a 1% difference be 'almost identical'?

The human genome has about 3,000 million 'letters'. *If* the 1% figure were correct, this would amount to 30 million letters difference, which would take 10 Bible-sized books to print. This is 50 times as much DNA as the simplest bacterium.[3] This is actually a huge difference that far exceeds the ability of even the most optimistic evolutionary scenarios to create, even given the claimed millions of years.[4]

What is the real difference?

The publication of the human and chimp DNA sequences made possible a comparison. However, even this is problematic because the chimp genome was not built from scratch. Small pieces of the chimp DNA were first sequenced; that is, the order of the chemical letters was determined using chemical procedures in laboratories. These small strings of 'letters' were

then aligned with the human genome in the places the evolutionists thought they should go (using computers to compare and place the segments). Then the human genome was removed, leaving a pseudo-chimp genome that *assumed common ancestry* (evolution), creating a mongrel sequence that is not real. The assumption of evolution in constructing the chimp genome in this way would make it look more like the human genome than it really is. But even with this evolutionary bias, the actual differences are *much* bigger than 1%.

In 2007 *Science* published an article on the similarity of human and chimp DNA titled, "Relative differences: the myth of 1%".[2] Author Jon Cohen queried the continued use of the 1% figure, citing comparisons following the publication of the draft chimp DNA sequence of around 5% difference. And yet the 1% myth is perpetuated in 2012 *in the same journal*.

Illustrating how wrong this is, in 2012 Drs Jeffrey Tomkins and Jerry Bergman reviewed the published studies comparing human and chimp DNA.[5] When *all* the DNA is taken into account and not just pre-selected parts, they found,

"it is safe to conclude that human-chimp genome similarity is not more than ~87% identical, and possibly not higher than 81%."

In other words, the differences are huge, possibly greater than 19%. Indeed, Dr Tomkins made his own thorough comparison and found the difference to be ~30%.[6] Also, the Y-chromosomes, found only in males, are radically different, contrary to evolutionists' expectations.[7]

Comparing two complex genomes is quite difficult. Assumptions have to be made about the importance of various parts of the DNA and the significance of different types of differences. For example, what do you do with human genes that are absent from chimps and vice versa? The tendency has been to ignore them and only compare the similar genes.

Many comparisons have involved only the protein-coding genes (only 1.2% of the DNA, and many protein-coding genes that are shared are indeed quite similar[8]), with the assumption that the rest of the DNA is 'not important' or even 'junk'. However, this view is no longer tenable; almost all the DNA probably has a function, again contrary to evolutionists' expectations.[9] But even if 'junk' DNA were non-functional, the differences here are much, much greater than in the protein-coding regions and must be included when assessing differences. We are *not* 99% identical; nothing like it.

What would any percentage similarity prove?

Neither evolutionists nor creationists made, or could make, predictions about the percent similarity before it was calculated. In other words, whether it was 99%, 95%, 70%, or whatever, evolutionists would still claim common ancestry and we creationists would see common design. In understanding the *implications* of these data, we are not dealing with hard science that can be shown by experiments; everyone is deriving a meaning based on a personal worldview.

However, the larger the difference between apes and humans, the bigger the problem in trying to explain it within the evolutionary timeframe, so evolutionists have good reason to try to play down the differences.

The myth persists

Comparison of whole genomes has revealed much greater differences than 1%, and yet the myth of 1% persists. Why? Why does *Science* perpetuate the myth in 2012? In 2007 Cohen cited geneticist Svante Pääbo, a chimp consortium member at the Max Planck Institute for Evolutionary Anthropology, Germany, as saying, "In the end, it's a political and social and cultural thing about how we see our differences."[2]

Perhaps evolutionists will not let go of the myth of 1% because it serves a political, social and cultural purpose? What would that purpose be, other than to deny the clear implication of DNA comparisons, which is that we are *very different from chimps*? The myth of similarity has been used to support the claim that humans have no special place in the world and even that chimps should be granted human rights.[10]

The large difference does not tally with evolutionary expectations but it is consistent with us being created *separately* from the animals. God made the first man from dust (Genesis 2:7) and the first woman from his rib (Genesis 2:22), not from any ape-like creature. And humans, unlike other creatures, were made in the image of God (Genesis 1:26, 27), a special creation. This image was not lost but marred at the Fall (see 'Broken Images', p. 86) so God made humans with a special purpose now and in eternity. ■

References and notes

1. Gibbons, A., Bonobos join chimps as closest human relatives, *Science Now,* 13 June 2012; news.sciencemag.org.
2. Cohen, J., Relative differences: the myth of 1%, *Science* **316**(5833):1836, 2007; doi: 10.1126/science.316.5833.1836.
3. The parasite *Mycoplasma genitalium* contains 521 genes (including 482 protein encoding genes) comprising 582,970 'letters'; Fraser, C.M. *et al.,* The minimal gene complement of *Mycoplasma genitalium, Science* **270**(5235):397–403, 1995 | doi:10.1126/science.270.5235.397.
4. Batten, D., Haldane's dilemma has not been solved, *J. Creation* **19**(1):20–21, 2005; creation.com/haldane.
5. Tomkins, J. and Bergman, J., Genomic monkey business—estimates of nearly identical human-chimp DNA similarity re-evaluated using omitted data, *J. Creation* **26**(1):94–100, April 2012; creation.com/chimp.
6. Tomkins, J., Comprehensive analysis of chimpanzee and human chromosomes reveals average DNA similarity of 70%, *Answers Research Journal* **6**(1):63–69, February 2013.
7. Catchpoole, D., Y chromosome shock, *Creation* **33**(2):56, 2011; creation.com/chimp-y.
8. Many proteins are very similar across a wide range of species, so comparing only protein-coding DNA tends to artificially accentuate similarity. Histones, which are involved in chromosome structure, and osteocalcin, which is a bone protein, are almost identical across many creatures. Differences between species seem to be due more to the non-protein-coding DNA that controls when and how much of the proteins are made. See Carter, R., Splicing and dicing the human genome, 1 July 2010; creation.com/splicing.
9. Batten, D., Dazzling DNA, *Creation* **35**(1):38, January 2013.
10. Cosner, L., Going ape about human rights: Are monkeys people, too? creation.com/goingape, 9 July 2008.

DON BATTEN, B.Sc.Agr.(Hons.), Ph.D.
Dr Batten worked as a research scientist and consultant plant physiologist and is now the C.E.O. of Creation Ministries International *in Brisbane, Australia. For more:* creation.com/batten.

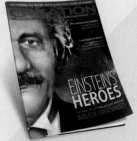

Article from
Creation **36**(1):35-37
January 2014

Article from
Creation **36**(3):52–55
July 2014

WHAT CAUSED THE ICE AGE?

Michael J. Oard

SECULAR SCIENTISTS have challenged creation scientists to explain the Ice Age. Also, they claim that there were numerous ice ages, possibly up to fifty, at intervals of 100,000 or 40,000 years over the past 2.6 million years.[1] Bible believers need to respond to this challenge by appealing to 1 Thessalonians 5:21: "Examine everything carefully; hold fast that which is good" (NASB). As we maintain confidence in God's word we need to carefully examine the observed data and be wary of how naturalism ('there is no God') has influenced its interpretations.

First we must establish whether there ever was an ice age. This is easy to do since there are hundreds of surface features in the mid and high latitudes similar to those around existing glaciers. They include terminal and lateral moraines (ridges of rock debris), scratched boulders, and scratched bedrock (figures 1 and 2). It is not possible for a moraine to be formed by liquid water.

Ice Age features are found on over 30% of the world's land mass, indicating past coverage by ice sheets or glaciers. Today only 10% is glaciated, mainly Antarctica and Greenland. There was only one (see "How many ice ages?" p. 48) and observations indicate that it was recent. Sharp crested moraines (figure 1) and scratched bedrock indicate youth. If the rocks were old, weathering should have rounded the moraines and erased the scratches in Figure 2.

The Ice Age is a major challenge to secular science

Often a challenge to creation scientists is also a challenge for secular scientists. In regard to the Ice Age, books and college professors sometimes falsely state it is easy for an Ice Age to develop: "It takes relatively little change to plunge us back into a situation where ice could start accumulating again on the fells [hills] and we are into a rapid downward spiral."[2]

But when we study the requirements for an ice age we find a different picture. Currently in most areas where there was once an ice sheet the winters are cold enough, but don't have even close to

enough snowfall. Springs, summers, and autumns would need to become significantly cooler than now to maintain the ice. Most challenging of all, these unusual conditions would need to last hundreds of years.

When we calculate how much spring and summer cooling would be needed, the picture becomes clearer. The temperatures would have to fall to below freezing on the average to maintain snow cover until the end of summer. Sunshine is the main cause of melting snow cover, even more effective than warmer temperatures. Summer sunshine at mid and high latitudes is intense. Using the net melting of snow and ice at low altitudes of the Antarctica Ice Sheet[3] as an example, the average temperature has to fall to about -7°C (20°F) for any winter and spring snow to last through the summer until the late autumn. This represents a cooling of about 19 Celsius degrees (34 Fahrenheit degrees) for the high latitudes of Scandinavia and Canada and about 28 Celsius degrees (50 Fahrenheit degrees) for the mid latitudes, such as the northern United States and along the southern edge of the ice sheet that developed in Europe and Asia.

Secular scientists propose that *present processes* or slight changes in the earth's orbital geometry could cause such cooling, but these have too small an effect. Even if cooler temperatures could be generated

this way, the air would then become about 60% drier. This would definitely interfere with snow development. So, there is a major problem in accounting for the massive amount of snow required for an ice age. And to make matters worse, even if by chance this climate change lasted a year, it would not fulfill the requirement of the climate change lasting for hundreds of years.

This is why the Ice Age is a major challenge for secular scientists. There are over 60 ideas (theories) on the origin of the Ice Age. That is why David Alt, professor of geology at the University of Montana, stated: "Although theories abound, no one really knows what causes ice ages."[4]

Can the Ice Age be explained within the biblical worldview?

Secular scientists really can't explain how an Ice Age happened, but can creation scientists? Yes, but first it needs to be placed within biblical earth history. The glacial features lie on top of sedimentary rock. This is a good indication that the Ice Age happened after the Flood. The conditions after the Flood were unique. Investigating them can help us find the answer.[5]

The Flood was a very catastrophic global event that included massive volcanism. So, after the Flood, numerous

Figure 1. Wallowa Lake horseshoe-shaped terminal and lateral moraine caused by a valley glacier descending out of the Wallowa Mountains and onto the plain near Enterprise, Oregon, USA. The lateral moraines are about 180 m (600 feet) high.

small volcanic particles were trapped high up in the atmosphere. These particles cooled the earth by reflecting sunlight back to space. But the volcanic particles would slowly settle out over several years. It is well accepted from the physical evidence that during the Ice Age there were many more volcanic eruptions than we have today. These would continually replenish the upper atmosphere with fine particles, probably stretching the cooling to several hundred years. So, the cooler summer requirement for the Ice Age is fulfilled. What about the second; where does the moisture for the required snowfall come from?

The Flood water was heated through volcanism (hot lava), and hot water was added by the "fountains of the great deep". The flood was a dynamic event, so after the Flood, the oceans would be mostly warm—from pole to pole and top to bottom. As a result there would be no sea ice on any of the oceans.

Warm water evaporates more quickly than cold; the warmer the water the quicker the evaporation. With the mid and high latitude oceans being much warmer than they are today, there would be many times more evaporation. As the moisture met the cooler continents it would trigger gigantic storms. This snow would dump

along and poleward of the jet stream and storm tracks. It would eventually turn into ice primarily by summer melting and refreezing. This fulfills the second criterion. Figure 3 shows all these events.

How long?

The third criterion, time, would be fulfilled, because in time evaporation would cool the oceans. And eventually volcanism would settle down. A cooler ocean would generate less moisture and less snow so the Ice Age would gradually wind down. Less volcanism would provide more sunshine, melting the ice sheets. Calculating the rate of cooling of the ocean after the Flood can give a rough estimate of the length of the Ice Age.

Based on the cooling of the oceans, the Ice Age could reach glacial maximum in about 500 years. It would have an average depth of about 700 m (2,300 ft) in the Northern Hemisphere and about 1,200 m (3,940 ft) over Antarctica, where most of the ice collected in the Southern Hemisphere.

Using the melting equation, we can figure out the ice sheet melting time. At first the ice would melt slowly then faster with giant lakes occurring at the edge of the ice. Some of these lakes broke causing

gigantic floods, such as the Lake Missoula flood in the northwest United States.[6] It would take only about 70 years to melt the ice sheets along the edge and about 200 years in interior Canada and Scandinavia. That is a total time of approximately 700 years for the Ice Age. We do not need a hundred thousand years for an ice age.

How many ice ages?

The secular idea of multiple ice ages comes from the belief that the earth's orbit changes slightly over millions of years but is cyclical, and that these cycles cause many ice ages. To buttress this idea, scientists sample the bottom of the oceans by dropping a tube into bottom sediments. They then analyze several variables in the sediment tube sample. The variables wiggle back and forth around an average. Since there are dozens of wiggles secular scientists simply assume that each wiggle is an ice age.

On land, most areas have evidence consistent with only one ice age. At the edge of the ice sheets, the glacial debris can be complicated, and it is here that they try to claim many ice ages. Yet, it is well known that the edge of an ice sheet advances, retreats, and surges rapidly forward creating complicated glacial sediments. It was admitted by five secular scientists that multiple ice ages are really an *assumption*.[7] Instead of three or four ice ages in Alberta, Canada, these scientists concluded that there was only one.

We can solve other challenges

Secular scientists have often challenged creationists to explain the Ice Age. This was met by accepting the biblical history and examining the data. This is an example of how we can solve other challenges to the Bible. We need to be seekers of truth (1 Thess. 5:21). Often we find the challenges we face are also challenges to secular scientists, although they often hide their difficulties. Having a correct understanding of a unique global Flood can solve many challenges presented by secular scientists with a commitment to the evolutionary/long-age paradigm. We need to be as committed to biblical earth history.

Figure 2. Scratched bedrock from an ice cap over the northern Rocky Mountains of Montana, USA. The ice moved east down the Sun River Canyon to scratch the bedrock.

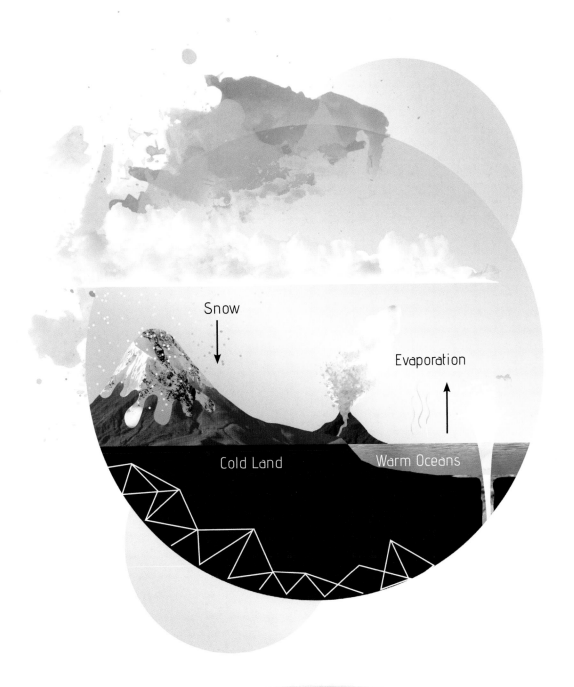

Snow

Evaporation

Cold Land

Warm Oceans

Figure 3. Heat trapped in the oceans after the Flood promoted high evaporation, which precipitated as snow and sleet on the continents. Ice continued to build up on the land for hundreds of years until the oceans cooled. This lessened the evaporation and so the ice sheets on the land melted back.

References and notes

1. Walker, M. and Lowe, J., Quaternary science 2007: a 50-year retrospective, *J. ological Society, London* **164(6)**:1,073–1,092, November 2007.

2. Smith, A., *The Ice Age in the Lake District: The Landscapes of Cumbria No. 3*, Riggs Side Publications, Keswick, Cumbria, England, p. 7, 2008.

3. Pickard, J., Comments on "Wastage of the Klutlan ice-cored moraines, Yukon Territory, Canada" by Driscoll (1980), *Quaternary Research* **22**(2):767–782, 1984.

4. Alt, D., *Glacial Lake Missoula and Its Humungous Floods*, Mountain Press, Missoula, Montana, p. 180, 2001.

5. Oard, M.J., *Frozen in Time: Woolly Mammoths, the Ice Age, and the Biblical Key to Their Secrets*, Master Books, Green Forest, Arkansas, 2004; Oard, M., *The Ice Age: Only the Bible Can Explain It!* CMI DVD, 2011; Oard, M., *The Great Ice Age*, Awesome Science Media DVD, 2013.

6. Oard, M.J., *The Missoula Flood Controversy and the Genesis Flood*, Creation Research Society Books, Chino Valley, Arizona, 2004. See also summary article in *Creation* **36**(2):43–46, 2014.

7. Young, R.R., *et al.* A single, late Wisconsin, Laurentide glaciation, Edmonton area and southwestern Alberta, *Geology* **22**:683–686, 1994.

A tale of

Carl Wieland

IMAGINE A colony of fleas living inside a motor car, the only home they have ever known. Two of them—let's call them **C** and **E**—begin to scientifically investigate this world of theirs. By studying the processes going on in the car, they discover all the basic laws of chemistry and physics—motion, gravity, electromagnetism, thermodynamics, quantum mechanics, and so on.

Everything they have learned can be proved by repeatable experiments, so they eventually agree on every conclusion. Finally, a young

Update: This article from the very early days of *Creation* magazine was thought to be very instructive, but unavailable to more recent subscribers in the days before the Internet. So it was updated and republished almost 20 years later in *Creation* **20**(3):45, 1998, which forms the basis for the version above.

Iurii Kovalenko/123RF

two fleas

flea asks them a fateful question: "How did this car come about in the first place?"

C: "That's obvious—it has been built at some time in the past by an intelligent designer."

E: "Whaaat? I never heard you talk like that before. Oh, I know, you're one of those religious cranks who believes in that book in the glove compartment, the manual, supposedly written by this designer. Don't you know that our best Fleabrew scholars now agree that it is a bunch of myths written by pre-scientific nomadic desert fleas?"

C: "How do you account for the car, then, without a maker?"

E: "Please don't get me wrong—you can believe in a maker if you wish, but you have to realize we can't teach that to young fleas in science classes. Obviously, the scientific processes and laws which we have been studying are and have been slowly and gradually building this car up from simpler substances."

C: "You must be aware of some of the tremendous scientific difficulties with such an idea."

E: "All scientific ideas have difficulties, and I'm working on these. But I'm open-minded enough to change my ideas on how this car evolved as further research results come in."

C: "Would you change your ideas on *whether* it evolved?"

E: "How could I? The only alternative to evolution of this car is its creation, and that would be a religious idea, not a scientific one. It would mean relying on a process (creation) which we can no longer observe, and a maker whom we cannot see. I'm surprised at a scientist like you holding to such mystical ideas."

C: "Actually, it's my science that's helped me to conclude that there must be a maker. You must realize that you can't run an experiment to prove your ideas either."

E: "Now that's unfair. You know how slowly iron filings are deposited into the crankcase—it would take hundreds of millions of years for them to coalesce into a new crankshaft. But at least we can see *something* happening."

C: "Your philosophy seems to stop you from even considering the possibility that there really is a car-maker. If there were, would you expect to be able to study the (past) processes of car-making, or the maker? Actually, I think the idea that there was a maker is much more scientifically valid than yours."

E: "What do you mean?"

C: "Well, the things we observe happening in the car fit better with the idea that it was once made and is now wearing out. Do you remember that second law of thermodynamics we discovered? Overall, everything in this car is wearing out, running down. None of the scientific processes that we have studied has the ability to make this car. I think this is very good evidence for creation. And this evidence is consistent with the book that claims to be the maker's manual, so it makes good sense to believe what it says.

"Another important evidence for creation is the organization of the components of this car—that is, the relationship between its parts. You see, a coil has no natural tendency to line up with a distributor and a spark plug in such a way as to make a spark—when these three parts work together, they are all obeying the laws of science—no mysterious processes are at work.

"Yet, everything we know about them forces us to the conclusion that they must have had that order, that relationship, that *purpose* if you like [**E** shudders at this point] imposed upon them from outside originally. This is positive evidence for creation. You yourself recognize evidence for creation—if you see a beautiful painting, say a Van Fleagh, you recognize it as the result of creative intelligence. You know *this* because you know that canvas and oils have no natural tendency to come together in that way. You recognize creation although you may never see the creator or the act of creation."

E: "I can see the point you're making, but … I refuse to believe there's anybody out there ■

Article from
Creation **20**(3):45
June 1998

World population figures tell a fascinating story. But it's not one that supports long-age belief.

WHERE ARE ALL THE PEOPLE?

Don Batten

OVER SEVEN billion people live on planet Earth. That sounds like a lot of people. Well, I would not want to invite them all to a barbecue at my house! However, they could all fit into an area the size of England, with about 20 square metres each. Many of us live in cities, so we have the impression that the world is bursting with people. However, much of the world is sparsely populated.

Nevertheless, many wonder at how the population could have grown to six billion from Noah's family who survived the Flood that wiped out everyone else about 4,500 years ago. When you do the figures, it confirms the biblical truth that everyone on Earth today is a descendant of Noah's sons and daughters-in-law. Not only that, but if people have been here for much longer, and there was no global Flood of Noah's day, there should be a lot more people than there are—or there should be a lot more human remains!

Many people have problems understanding growth *rates* of things. When the population doubles from 16 to 32, it does not seem like much, but when it doubles from three billion to six billion it seems like a lot more. But, it is exactly the same *rate* of growth. Given enough generations, the number of people being added with each generation becomes astronomical. It's like compound interest on an investment—eventually the amount being added each year becomes very great.

To illustrate this, think of the story of the inventor of chess. His king offered him a reward, but instead of gold he asked for one grain of rice doubled for each successive square on a chessboard. The number of grains would have been 1, 2, 4, 8, 16, 32 etc. The 10th square would have 512; the 20th, 524 *thousand;* the 30th, 537 *million.* The amount of rice on the last square[1] would have been a number so great—vastly in excess of the total world rice harvest at present—that it would have represented wealth far exceeding that of the king. Such is the power of compounding. And population growth is compound growth—that's why

so many people are now being added each year. It's not necessarily that people are having more children than they once did, or that fewer people are dying.

What causes population growth?

The population grows when more people are born than die. The current growth rate of the world population is about 1.7% per year.[2] In other words, for every 100 million people, 1.7 million are added every year; i.e. births net of deaths.

Many assume that modern medicine accounts for the world's population growth. However, 'third world' countries contribute most of the population growth, suggesting that modern medicine is not as important as many think.

Population growth in a number of South American and African countries exceeds 3% per year. In many industrialized countries with modern medical facilities, the population growth is less than 0.5%. Some relatively wealthy countries are actually declining in population.

The move from agriculture to manufacturing/ technology has been a big factor in slowing population growth in industrialized countries. Farmers needed to have sons to help with the farm work. This was particularly necessary before mechanization. My own family records show that in the early to mid-1800s in Australia, couples commonly had 8–10 surviving children. One couple had 16! And this was before the discovery of the germ basis of disease,[3] aseptic surgery,[4] vaccines[3] and antibiotics. Opportunity to expand, combined with biology, saw growth in population of 4% or more, *plus* increases due to immigration. High rates of population growth were also seen in Quebec, Canada, from 1760 to 1790, following the British conquest of Canada in 1759,[5] and well before the impact of modern medical knowledge.

In industrialized countries, the advent of social security pensions and retirement plans (superannuation) has probably been another major factor in the decline of population growth. These schemes mean that people do not see the need to have children for security in their old age. Furthermore, people can now easily choose how many children they have because of modern birth control methods, such as the contraceptive pill.

What growth rate is needed to get six billion people since the Flood?

It is relatively easy to calculate the growth rate needed to get today's population from Noah's three sons and their wives, after the Flood. With the Flood at about 4,500 years ago, it needs less than 0.5% per year growth.[6] That's not very much.

Of course, population growth has not been constant. There is reasonably good evidence that growth has been slow at times—such as in the Middle Ages in Europe. However, data from the Bible (Genesis 10–11) shows that the population grew quite quickly in the years immediately after the Flood. Shem had five sons, Ham had four, and Japheth had seven. If we assume that they had the same number of daughters, then they averaged 10.7 children per couple. In the next generation, Shem had 14 grandsons, Ham, 28 and Japheth, 23, or 130 children in total. That is an average of 8.1 per couple. These figures are consistent with God's command to "be fruitful and multiply and fill the earth" (Genesis 9:1).

Let us take the average of all births in the first two post-Flood generations as 8.53 children per couple. The average age at which the first son was born in the seven post-Flood generations in Shem's line ranged from 35 to 29 years (Genesis 11:10–24), with an average of 31 years for the named descendants, so a generation time of 40 years is reasonable. Hence, just four generations after the Flood would see a total population of over 3,000 people (remembering that the longevity of people was such that Noah, Shem, Ham, Japheth, etc., were still alive at that time). This represents a population growth rate of 3.7% per year, or a doubling time of about 19 years.[7]

If there were 300 million people in the world at the time of Christ's Resurrection,[2] this requires a population growth rate of only 0.75% since the Flood, or a doubling time of 92 years—much less than the documented population growth rate in the years following the Flood.

What if people had been around for one million years?

Evolutionists claim that mankind evolved from apes about a million years ago. If the population had grown at just 0.01% per year since then (doubling only every 7,000 years), there could be 10^{43} people today—that's a number with 43 zeros after it. This number is so big that not even the Texans have a word for it! To try to put this number of people in context, say each individual is given 'standing room only' of about 1 m² per person. However, the land surface area of the whole Earth is 'only' 1.5×10^{14} m². If every one of those square metres were made into a world just like this one, all these worlds put together would still 'only' have a surface area able to fit 10^{28} people in this way. This is only a tiny fraction of 10^{43} (10^{29} is 10 times as much as 10^{28}, 10^{30} is 100 times, and so on). Those who adhere to the evolutionary story argue that disease, famine and war kept the numbers almost constant for most of this period, which means that mankind was on the brink of extinction for most of this supposed history. This stretches credulity to the limits.

Where are all the bodies?

Evolutionists also claim there was a 'Stone Age' of about 100,000 years when between one million and 10 million

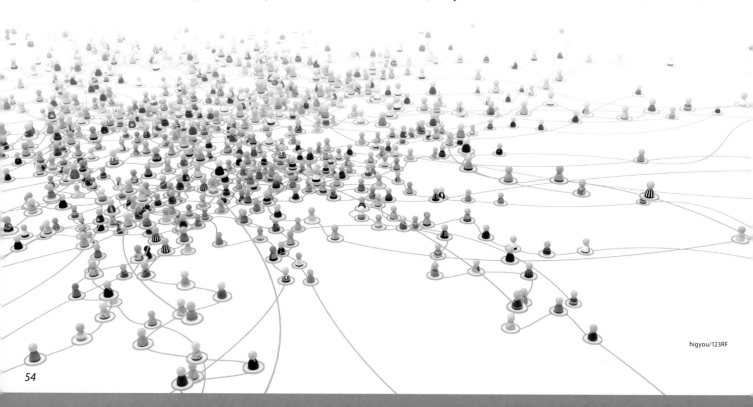

higyou/123RF

people lived on Earth. Fossil evidence shows that people buried their dead, often with artefacts—cremation was not practised until relatively recent times (in evolutionary thinking). If there were just one million people alive during that time, with an average generation time of 25 years, they should have buried 4 billion bodies, and many artefacts. If there were 10 million people, it would mean 40 billion bodies buried in the earth. If the evolutionary timescale were correct, then we would expect the skeletons of the buried bodies to be largely still present after 100,000 years, because many ordinary bones claimed to be much older have been found. However, even if the bodies had disintegrated, lots of artefacts should still be found.

Now the number of human fossils found is nothing like one would expect if this 'Stone Age' scenario were correct. The number found is more consistent with a 'Stone Age' of a few hundred years, which would have occurred after Babel. Many people groups could have used stone tools as they moved out from Babel (Genesis 11), having lost the technologies of metal smelting (Genesis 4:22) due to the Flood and the confusion of languages at Babel.

Immigrant peoples, when they settled in a new area, would have had an initial phase where they would shelter in caves, or have rudimentary housing. They would have made use of stone tools, for example, while they developed agricultural techniques appropriate to the local soils and climate, found sources of ores, and rediscovered how to manufacture tools, etc.

Groups that descended into animism might never emerge from this 'stone age' of their development,

because of the stifling effects of such things as taboos, and fear of evil spirits. One tribal group in the Philippines, for example, had a taboo against water, causing rampant disease due to lack of hygiene—before the Gospel of Jesus Christ rescued them from superstition.　■

References and notes

1. For the nth square, the number of rice grains = $2^{n-1} = 2^{63}$ for the last square, or about 10^{19} grains!
2. *Encyclopædia Britannica CD 2000*, Trends in world population.
3. Proven/developed by the creationist scientist Louis Pasteur (see Louis Pasteur (1822–1895), *Creation* **14**(1):16–19; creation.com/pasteur).
4. Pioneered by another great creationist scientist, Joseph Lister (see Joseph Lister: father of modern surgery, *Creation* **14**(2):48–51; creation.com/lister).
5. Armstrong, H.L., More on growth of a population, *Creation Research Society Quarterly* **22**(1):47,1985, citing Lower, A.R.M., *Canadians in the Making,* Longmans, Green and Co., Toronto, p. 113, 1958.
6. If r = % rate of growth per year, and the number of years of growth = n, then after n years, the population produced by the eight survivors of the Flood = $8(1+r/100)^n$.
7. The 'rule of 72' states that dividing 72 by the annual growth (in %) gives the years to double the population. This is an approximation that makes the calculations easy. A figure of 69.3 is more accurate ($100 \times \ln 2 = 69.3$).

Article from
Creation **23**(3):52–55
June 2001

Don Batten

MY CHILDHOOD best friend looked so much like me that our teachers, and even our friends, had a lot of trouble telling us apart. "Are you twins?", we were often asked. However, there was no family connection as far back as anyone could trace. The similarity in our appearance was not due to being closely related—or, putting it another way—due to us having a recent common ancestor, like a common father, grandmother, or even great grandparent. It was just a 'fluke'.

The main (only?) argument for evolution is that similarities between living things are due to relatedness, or common ancestry. If two kinds of animals share a lot of common features, then they are 'obviously' closely related and so must have had a recent common ancestor—or so the evolutionary reasoning goes. Birds, for example, all lay eggs, have feathers and a specialized lung comprised of interconnected air sacs, so the evolutionist would say all birds had a common ancestor which had these features. Creationists would say that birds have these similarities because they were created with a common basic plan. People would assume that because my friend and I were so similar we must have shared a very recent common ancestor—like the same parents. They were wrong. In like manner, the evolutionists are often—not always—wrong in assuming similarity is due to common ancestry.

Of course my friend and I are members of the same human kind and so we know that we had a common ancestor—who was a descendant of Japheth, in this case. However, the analogy is accurate—that the *degree* of similarity in appearance does not necessarily indicate the *degree* of genetic relatedness. As we shall see, evolutionists are forced to recognise this at times, but they (illogically) do not admit that such recognition undermines the main argument for evolution (if similarities occur that clearly are not due to common ancestry, how does the evolutionist know that *any* similarities are due to evolution?).

If living things had a common creator/designer, we would expect there to be many similarities—just like the early Porsche and VW 'beetle' have many similarities because they shared the same designer. If there were not these similarities in living things, we might be inclined to believe in many creators, not just one. The Bible tells us that God's very nature is revealed to us in what He has created (Romans 1:18-23). I believe that God

ARE LOOK ALIKES RELATED?

Article from
Creation **19**(2):39–41
March 1997

created things in such a way that the patterns we see defy a natural explanation—such as evolution—but support a supernatural explanation. In other words, the patterns of similarity cannot be consistently explained by any naturalistic (everything-made-itself) theory.

The more similar creatures are, according to the evolutionary argument, the more closely they should be related—that is, the more recent it is since they had the same ancestor. Take, as an example, the usual textbook illustration of the similarities between the limbs of animals with backbones (vertebrates) and people. Human beings have a five-finger/toe hand/foot (pentadactly) pattern, and limbs with two bones attached to the hand/foot joined to a single other major limb bone. We share this pattern with bats and frogs and therefore, the evolutionist argues, we must share five-digited common ancestors with these animals. That explains the similarities, we are told.

However, if we look at the horse limb (right), we see that it is quite different to the human form. Frogs and people have remarkably similar limb structures, but horses, which are supposedly very much more closely related to humans, have a limb with little resemblance to the human limb. Just on the basis of limb structures, it might be reasonable to suppose that frogs and people are more closely related than people and horses.

However, horses, as mammals, share many similarities to humans which frogs, as amphibians, don't share—horses, like us, are warm-blooded, give birth to live young, suckle their young, have hair, etc. The evolutionist claims that horses and humans must be more closely related than frogs and humans.

But what about the remarkable differences in the limbs of horses and humans? The evolutionist 'explains' the profound differences in the horse and human limbs as due to 'adaptation' in the horse. So, when the evolutionist confronts anomalies like the horse limb, a story is invented to 'explain' it. In this case the story is 'adaptation'. The limb was supposedly 'modified' by natural selection to do a different job. However, this is a just-so story to explain away evidence which does not fit the common ancestry idea.

QUOLLS AND CATS

Marsupials are mammals which give birth to very immature babies which are suckled in a protective pouch. These include the kangaroos, koalas, wombats and possums of Australasia and the opossums of the Americas. Placental mammals nurture their young in the womb, which develops an elaborate nourishing structure called a placenta. The babies are

Depositphotos/Artzzz

MANY CREATURES SHOW SIMILAR FEATURES
BECAUSE THEIR CREATOR USED SIMILAR STRUCTURES FOR SIMILAR PURPOSES

Australian marsupial wombat (left) and a marmot (right).

Sugar gliders (left) look similar to flying squirrels (right).

The extinct marsupial thylacine (left) and the wolf (right).

MARSUPIAL	PLACENTAL
Tasmanian 'Tiger' or Thylacine	Wolf
Feathertail Glider	Flying squirrel
Dunnart or Marsupial mouse	Mouse, Shrew
Cuscus	Monkey
Marsupial mole	Golden mole of Africa
Quoll	Cat
Bilby	Hare
Rat kangaroo	Rat
Wombat	Marmot
Numbat	Anteater

Table 1. Some marsupial and placental animals showing remarkable similarities

born in quite a developed state compared to marsupials.

Nearly all the mammals in Australia are marsupials. Why is this so? The evolutionist claims to have an answer: the marsupials evolved in Australia from a common ancestor which just happened to be here. Placental mammals—such as dogs, cats, horses, squirrels, mice, etc., evolved on other continents. That's the story.[1]

However, there are many incredible similarities between marsupial and placental animals which defy this naturalistic story. Take the marsupial mouse, or dunnart, and placental mouse, for example. Some types are so similar it is difficult to tell them apart without close inspection to look for the pouch.

The marsupial mole from the Northern Territory of Australia is incredibly similar to the golden mole of Africa. When the cuscus was first discovered in Papua New Guinea it was mistaken for a type of monkey. It has a flat monkey-like face, opposable digits on front and hind limbs, and a prehensile (grasping) tail.

The number of similar marsupial and placental animals is astounding, if they just arose by the evolutionary processes of chance mutations and natural selection.

The list could be extended by including extinct types such as the marsupial diprotodon, a hippopotamus-like creature. So there are many similarities which are not due to common ancestry, or evolution. How does the evolutionist account for these similarities? Here another story comes into play: many of the marsupials and placentals ended up looking like one another because they happened to be in similar ecological niches and so evolved similarly to fill those similar niches. This is another 'just-so' story. Such similarities are said to be due to 'convergence' or 'parallel evolution'. 'Convergence' is really just a grab bag to put similarities which cannot be explained through common ancestry (evolution). This is supposed to account for similarities

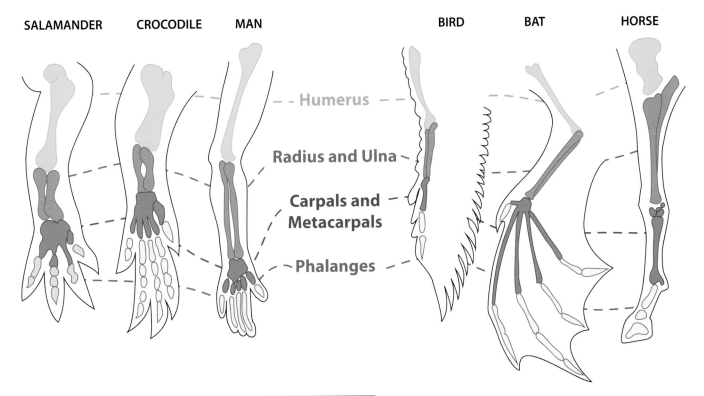

SALAMANDER   CROCODILE   MAN   BIRD   BAT   HORSE

- Humerus -
Radius and Ulna
Carpals and Metacarpals
Phalanges

HOMOLOGY

Specialists in the classification of organisms (taxonomists) call the similarities between organisms which are thought to be due to relatedness *homologies*.[1] (If the similar structures are not explainable by relatedness, then they are called *homoplasies*.) Evolutionists explain this by a common ancestor *with that feature*. E.g. the 5-digit pattern as evidence for their common ancestry from a 5-digited creature. Yet the nearest creatures they have to a common ancestor *did not have five digits!* *Acanthostega* had eight, while *Ichthyostega* had seven.

However, the homology concept is quite valid for creationists to apply in defining what were the original created kinds—where there is genuine relatedness amongst the descendants. For example, the many different species of *Eucalyptus* trees are probably one created kind. Likewise there are various types of cattle which are almost certainly the one biblical kind, as are big and small cats, and the false killer whale and bottlenose dolphin.[2]

REFERENCES AND NOTES

1. Statham, D., Homology made simple, *Creation* **34**(4):43–45, 2012; creation.com/homology-simple.
2. Batten, D., Ligers and Wholphins: what next?, *Creation* **22**(3):28–33, 2000; creation.com/ligers.

which do not fit the evolutionary scheme of descent based on other similarities.

It stretches the bounds of credulity to believe that so many marsupials just happened, without any plan and purpose, to look so similar to their placental counterparts. It's like trying to believe that two artists painted a series of almost identical paintings without reference to one another, or that the similarities between a VW and Porsche were not due to their having a common designer.

Also, if being in a similar ecological niche automatically generates similarities, why is the kangaroo not more like cattle, horses or deer—the kangaroo's ecological counterparts on other continents? The kangaroo throws a spanner into the logic of the 'convergence' story used to explain similarities which do not fit the evolutionary story.

God has indeed created things in such a way as to confound naturalistic (everything made itself) explanations for the origin of organisms. Various *ad hoc*, or just-so, stories have been invented in an attempt to explain the many things which do not fit the evolutionary scheme, but they are just that— stories. May God receive the glory that is His due for the marvelous things He has created! ■

REFERENCES AND NOTES

1. However, there is a problem for evolutionists in their fossil distribution. "Living marsupials are restricted to Australia and South America … In contrast, metatherian [marsupial] fossils from the Late Cretaceous are exclusively from Eurasia and North America … This geographical switch remains unexplained." Cifelli, R.L. and Davis, B.M., Marsupial origins, *Science* **302**:1899-1902, 2003.

■ **Don Batten**

SOME FOLK just don't see the significance of the myriad examples of 'living fossils'. Following our interview with Dr Carl Werner on the topic,[1] one evolutionist protested: "There is no written rule that says a lineage has to die out just because an offspring develops a beneficial mutation. The theory of evolution explains how species change over time, it doesn't say that all species must change over time. As long as a species can survive in its environment and pass on its genetic information to its offspring, it can survive indefinitely. It doesn't mean that the 'living fossil' didn't speciate, it just means those possible splits died out while the original lineage was able to always successfully reproduce even into today. How exactly does that not work with evolution?"

However, as Dr Werner said in the article:

"If a scientist believes in evolution and sees fossils that look like modern organisms at the dinosaur digs, he/she might invent an hypothesis to 'explain' living fossils this way: 'Yes I believe that animals have changed greatly over time (evolution), but some animals and plants were so well adapted to the environment that they did not need to change. So I am not bothered at all by living fossils.' This added hypothesis says that some animals did not evolve. But if a theory can be so flexible, adding hypotheses that predict the opposite of your main theory, one could never disprove the theory. The theory then becomes unsinkable, and an unsinkable theory is not science."[1]

Furthermore, some evolutionists have admitted that living fossils ('stasis') are a big problem for evolution.[2] They have no explanation. This is not about suggesting that something has to go extinct if something evolves from it; that is not the point. The point is the *lack of change*, which is a huge problem for evolution, which is about *vast changes*. As high-profile evolutionists Stephen Jay Gould and Niles Eldredge admitted, "the maintenance of stability within species must be considered as a major evolutionary problem."[3]

Evolutionists like to call it 'evolutionary stasis'. But evolution is about *change,* and putting 'evolutionary' in front of 'stasis'does not *explain* stasis in terms of evolution.[4] All organisms undergo mutations (accidental genetic changes). There is no mechanism that prevents mutations such that many organisms can remain the same for supposedly hundreds of millions of years.

And as if explaining the stasis exhibited by living 'dino era' creatures such as horseshoe crabs (pictured here) wasn't already hard enough for evolutionists, what about far 'older' examples such as fossil ostracodes (clam-like arthropods known as 'seed shrimps'), complete with exceptionally well-preserved soft body parts.[5] With an evolutionary 'age' of 425 million years, the fossilized ostracodes look just the same as living ostracodes today.[6] *425 million years of stasis!?* In that alleged time-frame, evolution by mutations and natural selection has supposedly changed some (unidentified) worm into all the species of fish, amphibians, reptiles, birds, mammals (including elephants and mice, and of course, us). At the same time all the land plants have supposedly evolved. Such is the claimed power of evolution to change things, and yet these ostracodes have remained unchanged (and many others 'dated' even older).

In the evolutionary story, environmental change, or the development of new environmental niches, drives evolution as organisms adapt to new environments. So they argue that living fossils are the creatures whose environment did not change. However, in the evolutionary view Earth has sustained multiple global catastrophes (but not a global flood; the Bible speaks about that!) and multiple ice ages. How could there be any place on earth that has remained environmentally static, including no change in predators? And living fossils occur across the spectrum of life; and they are very common.

Combine the *observations* of stasis and the scarcity of transitional fossils (there should be millions of them) and you have to ask, "Where is the fossil *evidence* for evolution?"

Well-preserved fossils speak of rapid burial in water-borne sediment, consistent with the Bible's account of the global Flood just 4,500 years ago. And stasis is right in line with the Creator having made creatures to reproduce "according to their kind", just as Genesis says happened during Creation week, about 6,000 years ago. *No* millions of years. *No* evolution. ■

EVOLUTIONISTS CAN'T

References and notes

1. Living fossils: a powerful argument for creation—Don Batten interviews Dr Carl Werner, author of *Living Fossils (Evolution: the Grand Experiment* vol. 2), *Creation* **33**(2):20–23, 2011.
2. See creation.com/living-fossils-enigma.
3. Gould, S. and Eldredge, N., Punctuated equilibrium comes of age, *Nature* **366**(6452):223–224, 1993.
4. See: Bell, P., Evolutionary stasis: Double-speak and propaganda, *Creation* **28**(2):38–40, 2006; creation.com/stasis.
5. Siveter, D., Sutton, M. and Briggs, D., An ostracode crustacean with soft parts from the Lower Silurian, *Science* **302**(5651):1749–1751, 2003.
6. Oard, M., Remarkable stasis of a fossil ostracode with soft parts, *J. Creation* **18**(3):16, 2004.

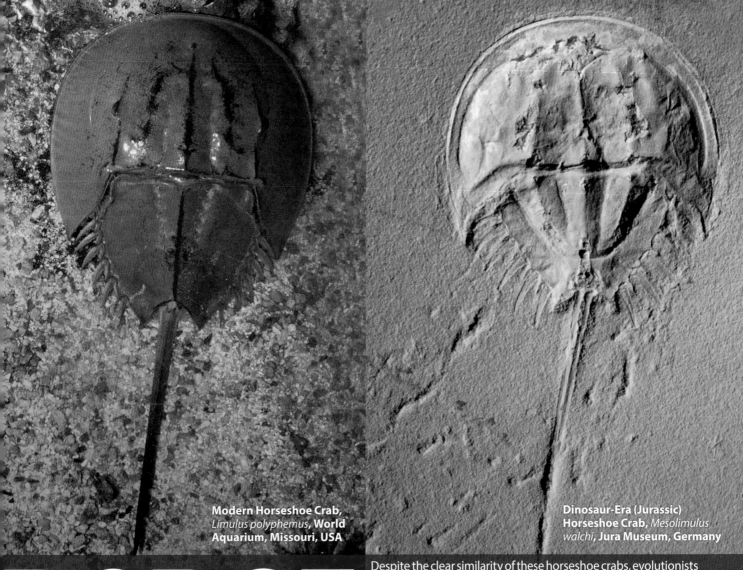

Modern Horseshoe Crab, *Limulus polyphemus***, World Aquarium, Missouri, USA**

Dinosaur-Era (Jurassic) Horseshoe Crab, *Mesolimulus walchi***, Jura Museum, Germany**

Despite the clear similarity of these horseshoe crabs, evolutionists insist on giving the fossil different genus and species names to its living counterpart. But where's the difference? Note that the fossil specimen was found in rock labelled as "Jurassic"—said to date from 180–225 million years ago. Why is there no evolution ('change') in all that (supposed) time?

DODGE 'LIVING FOSSILS'

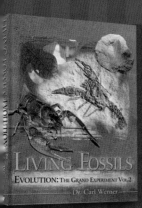

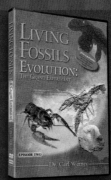

These photos are from Dr Carl Werner's book, *Living Fossils—Evolution the Grand Experiment* Vol. 2 (p. 51), and the superb documentary DVD (pictured right), available from **creation.com/store**.

This astounding *Living Fossils* DVD documentary shows that many modern animals and plants occur as fossils in rock layers that are 'dinosaur era'. Yet museums don't portray dinosaurs with modern organisms, reinforcing evolutionary ideas of origins. *Living Fossils* provides powerful evidence that microbes-to-man evolution never happened.

Article from *Creation* **33**(4):42–43 October 2011

Dominic Statham

IF TWO students hand in an assignment containing exactly the same mistakes, their teacher will rightly suspect that one (or both) has been copying the other's work. This is because the chance of them independently making the same mistakes is very small. Similarly, when an identical mutation is found in the DNA of apes and humans, evolutionists claim that the only reasonable explanation is that the mutation occurred in a common ancestor and was then passed down to its descendants.

There are many parts of our DNA that look like virus DNA, and some evolutionists argue that this shows that these parts of our DNA *came* from viruses. Our ancestors, they say, were infected by viruses which added DNA to our ancestors' DNA, and this was then passed down to us. These short stretches of genetic material are often referred to as ERVs (**e**ndogenous **r**etro**v**iruses; see box) and

are said to be 'junk' having no useful purpose. Since we sometimes find the same ERVs in the same locations in the DNA of apes and humans, evolutionists claim that ERVs provide strong evidence for evolution. The probability, they say, of the same viruses randomly inserting the same stretches of DNA in the same locations in human and ape DNA is negligible. It is far more likely, they say, that a common ancestor passed on its ERVs to both humans and apes.

As convincing as it sounds, however, closer examination reveals serious flaws in this argument.

Are ERVs really junk?

Given the number of times that evolutionists have had to backtrack on their claim that our bodies are full of junk, one would think they would by now have learnt their lesson. For example, dozens of organs were wrongly labelled 'vestigial', said to be non-functional leftovers from our

evolutionary past. Organs such as the appendix were said to have been used by our ancestors millions of years ago but, over the course of evolution, had become redundant. However, most if not all of these 'vestigial organs' now have known functions.[1] Similarly, evolutionists claimed that much of our DNA has no function; but recent research indicates that this is nonsense.[2] Significantly, functions of many ERVs have also been discovered, and they are known to interact with the rest of our DNA in a particularly sophisticated manner. For example, they enable the same stretches of DNA to be read and used in different ways. Research indicates they play an active role in at least one-fifth of our DNA.[3]

Did ERVs come from viruses?

When seeking to explain observations, good scientists must think laterally. We should therefore ask the question, "Did ERVs come from viruses or did these

"Did ERVs come from viruses or did these viruses actually come from ERVs?"

viruses actually come from ERVs?" How can evolutionists 'know' that ERVs came from viruses?

Since many ERVs have already been found to be functional, it is reasonable to think that they are there by design. The fact that we find the same ERVs in humans and apes is really no surprise. If humans and apes share the same creator and were made to live in the same world and to eat the same sort of food, it is hardly surprising that they were made with similar DNA (although the differences are *much* greater than evolutionists expected, which is a major problem for their story[4]).

As with all alleged evidence for evolution, the argument may appear convincing when first presented. However, when we scratch beneath the surface, a very different picture emerges—and one that is entirely consistent with a belief in biblical creation. As scientists make the effort to study ERVs, more of their functions are becoming known, indicating that they are

not junk. Moreover, evidence is mounting that they play crucial roles (for example in embryonic development)[5,6] and in controlling the way DNA works. The same ERVs are found in humans and apes because we share a common designer rather than a common ancestor.

More mistakes about mistakes

Sometimes genes *appear* to have become non-functional due to mutations, and are referred to as 'pseudogenes'. Since we sometimes find the same mutations in the same 'pseudogenes' in humans and apes, it is argued that this must be due to humans and apes sharing a common ancestor. The probability, they say, of the same mutations occurring independently in humans and apes is just too small. Again, however, this argument—which evolutionists thought so conclusive—is losing its teeth.

Firstly, functions of 'pseudogenes' are being discovered, indicating that

at least some are not 'pseudogenes' at all; perhaps few, if any, will turn out to be truly functionless. For example, they have been found to produce proteins, switch genes off when they're not needed, and control the amounts of proteins that are to be made.[7] Following a major research project studying human DNA (the ENCODE[8] project), some geneticists have suggested that probably very little (if any) of our DNA is non-functional.[9] This undermines both the ERV and the pseudogene arguments.

Secondly, geneticists now realise that mutations often do not occur randomly, and certain parts of DNA are more susceptible to mutation that others. These are known as 'hotspots'. In some cases, it *might* be true that the same mutations occurred independently in humans and apes; but this is not surprising if they are at 'hotspots'.[10]

It seems that as our knowledge of human DNA increases, the case for

SEMI-TECHNICAL

What is a virus?

Viruses are tiny infectious agents that can reproduce only by hijacking the machinery inside the cells of the plant or animal they infect. Lacking a ribosome, for example, they are unable to manufacture proteins unaided. They also have no way of producing the essential energy unit, ATP, required to assemble proteins from amino acids.

What is a retrovirus?

Some viruses are made up from DNA and others from RNA. In the normal working of the cell, RNA for protein manufacture is produced from DNA. So viruses which contain only RNA must reverse this process and first produce a DNA copy of their RNA. These viruses are called 'retroviruses' (from the Latin word *retro* meaning 'backwards'). The virus then implants this DNA into the infected cell and uses the cell's machinery to reproduce itself.

What is an endogenous retrovirus (ERV)?

'Endogenous retroviruses' are said to be sequences of DNA, derived from retrovirus RNA, that have found their way into germ cells (sperm or eggs) and have thereby been passed down to the descendants of the infected organism. They are 'endogenous' because they are said to have become 'endogenized', i.e. integrated into the descendants' genome (from the Greek words *endo* meaning 'within' and *genous* meaning 'producing'). The term 'endogenous retrovirus', however, is unfortunate because it assumes a particular explanation for their origins. Creationist molecular biologist Ian Macreadie (Associate Professor at RMIT University, Melbourne, Australia) sees retroviruses as genetic material that escaped from cells, rather than the originators of ERVs.[1,2]

Are all viruses harmful?

Some bacteria and viruses are very beneficial and were likely created by God in the beginning. For example, bacteria are essential for decomposing organic matter, enabling old plant material to be recycled. They also help us digest our food. Viruses can increase plants' tolerance to heat and drought,[3] destroy cancer cells,[4] and help keep soil fertile. Just as bees carry pollen from flower to flower, viruses can transfer genes between bacteria, enabling them to perform their many useful functions.[5] Harmful versions of these bacteria and viruses are probably degenerate forms of originally benevolent designs that arose after sin entered the world (Genesis 3).

References and notes

1. Wieland, C. and Batten, D., Creation in the research lab: An interview with leading Australian molecular biologist and microbiologist Ian Macreadie, *Creation* **21**(2):16–17, March 1999; creation.com/macreadie.
2. See also Borger, P., The design of life: part 3—an introduction to variation-inducing elements, *J. Creation* **23**(1):99–106, April 2009; creation.com/vige-introduction.
3. Roosink, M.J., Beneficial microbes for agriculture, The Samuel Roberts Noble Foundation, October 2008; noble.org.
4. Kim, M., Biological view of viruses: creation vs evolution, *J. Creation* **20**(3):12–13, 2006; creation.com/bioviruses.
5. Bergman, J., Did God make pathogenic viruses? *J. Creation* **13**(1):115–125, April 1999; creation.com/viruses.

evolution gets weaker and weaker. It's a theory that thrives on ignorance.

Conclusion

'Shared mistakes' would only provide evidence for evolution if they really were mistakes *and* if they had been shown conclusively to have occurred randomly. It is increasingly doubtful that DNA is littered with such mistakes, as has been suggested in the past, and geneticists now realise that it cannot be assumed that a particular mutation has occurred randomly.

Evolutionists very readily accept evidence for evolution without carefully considering alternative explanations for the data. Experience has shown that supposedly unanswerable arguments for evolution quickly fall as more facts become known. ■

References and notes

1. creation.com/vestigial-qa.
2. Statham, D.R., More nails in the coffin of 'junk DNA'; creation.com/junk-dna-functions.
3. Doyle, S., Large scale function of 'endogenous retroviruses', *J. Creation* **22**(3):16, December 2008; creation.com/functions-erv.
4. Batten, D., The myth of 1%, *Creation* **36**(1):35–37, January 2014.
5. Mallet, F. *et al.,* The endogenous retroviral locus ERVWE1 is a bona fide gene involved in hominoid placental physiology, *PNAS* **101**(6):1731–1736, 2004; pbil.univ-lyon1.fr/members/duret/publications/PDF/2004-Mallet-PNAS.pdf | doi:10.1073/pnas.0305763101.
6. National Centre for Biotechnology Information, ERVW-1 endogenous retrovirus group W, member 1 [*Homo sapiens* (human)]; ncbi.nlm.nih.gov.
7. Wells, J., *The Myth of Junk DNA*, pp. 91–92, Discovery Institute Press, Seattle, 2011.
8. ENCODE stands for **Enc**yclopedia **o**f **D**NA **E**lements.
9. Batten, D., Dazzling DNA, *Creation* **35**(1):38, 2013; creation.com/dazzling-dna.
10. Truman, R., and Borger, P., Why the shared mutations in the hominidae exon X gulo pseudogene are not evidence for common descent, *J. Creation* **21**(3):118–127, 2007; creation.com/gulo_appendix.

DOMINIC STATHAM,
B.Sc., D.I.S., M.I.E.T., C.Eng.
spent twenty-five years working as an engineer in the aeronautical and automotive industries. He is now a speaker/writer for CMI-UK/Europe. For more: creation.com/dominic-statham.

"Supposedly unanswerable arguments for evolution quickly fall as more facts become known."

Article from
Creation **36**(4):52–55
October 2014

THE AM

AZING MOTORIZED GERM

Steven DeVowe

WHAT DO your skin, a compost pile, and Lake Superior all have in common? Each of them is home to an abundance of microscopic germs, properly called bacteria. Bacteria seem to be thought of as 'simple' compared to many-celled organisms, but certain motorized bacteria (such as *E. coli* or *Spirilla*) reveal immense engineering complexity.

Efficient design

These motorized bacteria are hardly 'simple'. The bacterium swims about with a whip-like cord called a *flagellum* (plural *flagella*), driven by a fantastic motor embedded in the outer shell. The flagellar motor is powered by proton flow, and closely resembles microscopic electric motors, powered by electron flow. The motor generates waves in the cord, which drive the germ forward.

A bacterial flagellar motor has the amazing quality of combining speed with efficiency. These extremely efficient motors can quickly stop, start, change speeds, and reach a top speed of about 100,000 rpm (revolutions per minute)![1] The cell is propelled up to 15 body-lengths per second at top speed. If this could be scaled up, it would be like a person of height 1.8 m (6 ft) swimming at 100 km/h (60 mph).

It is also very versatile, because it has forward and reverse gears, enabling the germ to reverse direction within a quarter of a turn.

Most man-made electric motors are up to 75–95% efficient at larger sizes, but lose efficiency as they get smaller.[2] The bacterial motor is almost 100% efficient at cruising speed. The bacterium uses only 2% of its total energy for swimming.

Microscopic design

Biological flagellum motors are also superior in their minute size—a clear example of *nanotechnology*. To view them, you need an electron microscope, because they are 25 nanometres (one millionth of an inch) in diameter.

Eight million of them would fit in the cross-sectional area of an average human hair. Scaling a regular electric motor to

Updates

Several discoveries made since this article have reinforced the design explanation, even if the discoverers made vacuous homages to evolution.

Clutch

Like most good motors, the flagellum has a *clutch* that disconnects the motor from the tail, as discovered by scientists from Indiana University Bloomington (IU) and Harvard University.[7] This is useful when the bacteria make biofilms; the spinning tail could disrupt it if not stopped.

The 'clutch' is a single protein, called EpsE, which interacts with one of the rotor proteins, called FliG. This changes the rotor's shape so that it disengages from the engine. This clutch mechanism is very efficient: it means that the germ needs to make only one protein to halt the powered filament motion, and this takes only 15 minutes. It also preserves the motor and tail intact, so they could be quickly reactivated if necessary, rather than needing to be rebuilt from scratch.[8]

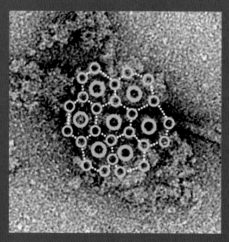

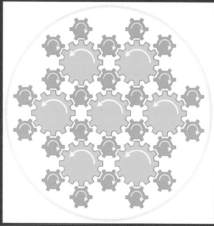

Diagrams: Proc Natl Acad Sci U S A. 2012 Dec 11; 109(50): 20643–20648.
Published online 2012 Nov 26. doi: 10.1073/pnas.1215274109

Seven motors combined to power one tail

It's hard enough to explain the design of one motor. But some germs have more than one flagellum. Sometimes they work individually but still the germ manages to coordinate the motors. Other germs have the tails loosely bundled.

But the marine bacterium MO-1 is different again. Here, seven flagella are tightly bundled in a sheath, as shown by a research team from French and Japanese universities.[9] And they surrounded by 24 fibrils (tiny fibres), in a hexagonal array. And these rotate in the opposite direction to the flagella, allowing them to rotate freely—so they are actually free-moving gear wheels! These gears or bearings combine the power of all seven motors into one tail, it can spin very fast. This enables the bacterium to swim about 300 µm/s, 10 times faster than *E. coli* and *Salmonella*.

Despite being evolutionists, the researchers referred to "this design" and "complex and exquisite architecture" of this system.[10]

this size would bog it down with friction, because water tends to get 'stickier' as things are smaller. But it does not cause any problems for the flagellar motor.

Purposeful design

There are no man-made motors that are as rapid, efficient, and small as flagellar motors in bacteria. Could such a motor that far exceeds man's inventions be the result of a cosmic accident billions of years ago? Every example of man-made electric motors proves to be primitively clumsy compared to the superior complexity and efficiency of the flagellum motor. The reasonable solution is that motorized bacteria had an all-wise designer, Jesus Christ our Creator (John 1:3; Hebrews 1:2).

"For the invisible things of him from the creation of the world are clearly seen, being understood by the things that are made, even his eternal power and Godhead; so that they are without excuse" (Romans 1:20). ■

References and notes

1. A good summary is by Howard Berg, a professor of molecular and cellular biology, and of physics, at Harvard University: Motile Behavior of Bacteria, *Physics Today*, 1999.
2. *Van Nostrand's Scientific Encyclopedia*, p. 2014, 8th edn, Van Nostrand Reinhold, New York, 1995.
3. Rennie, J., 15 answers to creationist nonsense, *Scientific American* **287**(1):78–85, July 2002; refutation after Sarfati J., *Refuting Evolution 2*, ch. 10, CBP, 2011.
4. *Unlocking the Mystery of Life*, DVD, Illustra Media, 2002.
5. Mecsas, J., and Strauss, E.J., Molecular Mechanisms of Bacterial Virulence: Type III Secretion and Pathogenicity Islands, *Emerging Infectious Diseases* 2(4), October–December 1996; cdc.gov/ncidod/EID/vol2no4/mecsas.htm.
6. Nguyen L. *et al.*, Phylogenetic analyses of the constituents of Type III protein secretion systems, *J. Mol. Microbiol. Biotechnol.* **2**(2):125–44, April 2000.
7. Blair, K.M., Turner, L., Winkelman, J.T., Berg, H.C. and Kearns, D.B., A molecular clutch disables flagella in the *Bacillus subtilis* biofilm, *Science* 320(5883):1636–1638, 20 June 2008 | doi: 10.1126/science.1157877.
8. Sarfati, J., Germ's miniature motor has a clutch, *J. Creation* 22(3):9–11, 2008; creation.com/clutch.
9. Ruan Juanfang and 8 others, Architecture of a flagellar apparatus in the fast-swimming magnetotactic bacterium MO-1, PNAS 26 November 2012 | doi:10.1073/pnas.1215274109.
10. Sarfati, J., Germ with seven motors in one! creation.com/7motors1, 15 January 2013.

Steven DeVowe
When he wrote this article, Steven DeVowe was a homeschooled student. Now he is a quality control inspector and founder of Victory Programming. *Steven is married with six children.*

How do evolutionists explain away such exquisite design?

Scientific American tried to explain this amazing miniature motor by evolution, by claiming that the parts were 'co-opted' from other functions, in particular, the 'type III secretory system' (TTSS) of some disease germs:

"The sophisticated components of this flagellum all have precedents elsewhere in nature …

"'In fact, the entire flagellum assembly is extremely similar to an organelle that Yersinia pestis, the bubonic plague bacterium, uses to inject toxins into cells. …

"The key is that the flagellum's component structures … can serve multiple functions that would have helped favor their evolution.'[3]

Scientific American's argument is like claiming that if the components of an electric motor already exist in an electrical shop, they could assemble by themselves into a working motor. However, the right organization is just as important as the right components.

Dr Scott Minnich of the University of Idaho, a world expert on the flagellar motor, disagrees with *Scientific American*. He says that his belief that this motor has been intelligently designed has given him many research insights. Minnich points out that the very process of assembly in the right sequence requires other regulatory machines.[4] He also points out that only about 10 of the 40 components can possibly be explained by co-option, but the other 30 are brand new.

Finally, Dr Minnich's research shows that the flagellum won't form above 37°C; instead, some secretory organelles form from the same set of genes. But this secretory apparatus, as well as the plague bacterium's drilling apparatus, are a degeneration from the flagellum. This makes sense: The flagellum assembly mechanism is designed to punch out the proteins required for the flagellum in a very orderly way. If this is *disabled*, it can punch out proteins (including toxins) in a *haphazard* way, as the TTSS does.

Another problem for *Scientific American's* evolutionary 'explanation' is that it is inconsistent with its own theory! Evolution teaches that bacteria evolved before the plants and animals that they could parasitize. So it makes sense that the swimming machinery preceded the secretion machinery that would be needed only once multicellular life evolved. Indeed, evolutionary specialists agree that the flagellum preceded the TTSS:

'It seems plausible that the original type III secretion system for virulence factors evolved from those for flagellar assembly."[5]

"We suggest that the flagellar apparatus was the evolutionary precursor of Type III protein secretion systems."[6]

So the *Scientific American* explanation is totally without merit, not only objectively but also within its own evolutionary framework. It is highly disingenuous for this magazine to propose an explanation that *defies even the best evolutionary theories,* without telling the readers.

Article from
Creation **27**(1):24–25
December 2004

RADIOCARBON IN DIAMONDS: ENEMY OF BILL

Jonathan Sarfati

Carbon

What do hard sparkling diamonds and dull soft pencil 'lead' have in common? They are both forms (allotropes) of carbon. Most carbon atoms are 12 times heavier than hydrogen (^{12}C), about one in 100 is 13 times heavier (^{13}C), and one in a trillion (10^{12}) is 14 times heavier (^{14}C). Of these different types (isotopes) of carbon, ^{14}C is called radiocarbon, because it is radioactive—it breaks down over time.

Radiocarbon dating

Some try to measure age by how much ^{14}C has decayed. Many people think that radiocarbon dating proves billions of years.[1] But evolutionists know it can't, because ^{14}C decays too fast. Its half-life ($t_{1/2}$) is only 5,730 years—that is, every 5,730 years, half of it decays away. After two half lives, a quarter is left; after three half lives, only an eighth; after 10 half lives, less than a thousandth is left.[2] In fact, a lump of ^{14}C as massive as the earth would have completely decayed in less than a million years.[3]

So if samples were really over a million years old, there would be no radiocarbon left. But this is not what we find, even with very sensitive ^{14}C detectors.[4]

Diamonds

Diamond is the hardest substance known, so its interior should be very resistant to contamination. Diamond requires very high pressure to form—pressure found naturally on earth only deep below the surface. Thus, they probably formed at a depth of 100–200 km. Geologists believe that the ones we find must have been transported supersonically to the surface in extremely violent eruptions through volcanic pipes. Otherwise, the diamond would anneal into graphite.[5] Some are found in these pipes, such as kimberlites, while other diamonds were liberated by water erosion and deposited elsewhere (called alluvial diamonds). According to evolutionists, the diamonds formed about 1–3 billion years ago.

Dating diamonds

Geophysicist Dr John Baumgardner, part of the RATE research group,[6] investigated ^{14}C in a number of diamonds.[7] There should be no ^{14}C at all if they really were over a billion years old, yet the radiocarbon lab reported that there was over 10 times the detection limit. Thus, they had a radiocarbon 'age' far less than a million years! Dr Baumgardner repeated this with six more alluvial diamonds from Namibia, and these had even more radiocarbon.

The presence of radiocarbon in these diamonds where there should be none is thus sparkling evidence for a 'young' world, as the Bible records. ∎

References and notes

1. For example, the 'Rev.' Barry Lynn, leader of the anti-Christian group Americans United for the Separation of Church and State, proclaimed in a nationally televised debate, 'Carbon dating, that shows the earth is billions of years old!' (*Firing Line*, PBS, 19 December 1997).
2. The time t since radioactive decay commenced can be given by $N/N_0 = e^{-\lambda t}$, where N is the number of atoms measured in the present; N_0 is the initial number; λ, the decay constant, which is related to the half life $t_{1/2}$ by $\lambda = \ln 2/t_{1/2}$. This presupposes that the system is closed, so that the loss of atoms is solely by decay, and that the decay rate is constant.

Article from
Creation **28**(4):26–27
September 2006

enki/123RF

Creation
NOAH'S FLOOD IN ANCIENT EPIC
Vision control
THE AMAZING ARMADILLO

3. The earth's mass is 6×10^{27} g; equivalent to 4.3×10^{26} moles of ^{14}C. Each mole contains Avogadro's number ($N_A = 6.022 \times 10^{23}$) of atoms. It takes only 167 halvings to get down to a single atom ($\log_2(4.3 \times 10^{26}$ mol $\times 6.022 \times 10^{23}$ mol$^{-1}) = \log_{10}(2.58 \times 10^{50}) / \log_{10}2$), and 167 half-lives is well under a million years.

4. AMS (accelerator mass spectrometry) counts the atoms themselves, and can detect one ^{14}C in more than 10^{16} atoms, or measure a $^{14}C/C$ ratio of $<10^{-16}$ or 0.01% of the modern ratio (0.01 pMC, percent modern carbon).

5. Snelling, A., Diamonds—evidence of explosive geological processes, *Creation* **16**(1):42–45, 1993; creation.com/ diamonds-explosive. Compare Diamond Science, diamondwholesalecorporation. com, accessed 22 May 2006.

6. Vardiman, L., Snelling, A., and Chaffin, E., *Radioisotopes and the Age of the Earth*, Vol. **2**, ch. 8, Institute for Creation Research, California, USA, 2005. Dr Baumgardner also investigated many coal samples, and they also turned out to have ^{14}C.

7. Baumgardner, J., Measurable ^{14}C in fossilized organic materials: confirming the young earth creation-flood model, 5th International Conference on Creationism, 2003; globalflood.org.

8. Rotta, R.B., Evolutionary explanations for anomalous radiocarbon in coal? CRSQ 41(2):104–112, September 2004. ^{14}C in coal was reported by: Baumgardner, J. *et al.*, The Enigma of the Ubiquity of ^{14}C in Organic Samples Older Than 100 ka, *Eos Transactions of the American Geophysical Union* **84**(46), Fall Meeting Suppl., Abstract V32C-1045, 2003. And also: Lowe, D., Problems associated with the use of coal as a source of 14C free background material, *Radiocarbon* **31**:117–120, 1989.

9. Giem, P., Carbon-14 content of fossil carbon, Origins **51**:6–30 (2001), grisda. org/origins/51006.htm.

OBJECTIONS (TECHNICAL) AND ANSWERS

1. The ^{14}C readings in the diamonds are the result of background radiation in the detector.

   This shows that the objector doesn't even understand the method. AMS doesn't measure radiation but counts atoms. It was the obsolete scintillation method that counted only decaying atoms, so was far less sensitive. In any case, the mean of the $^{14}C/C$ ratios in Dr Baumgardner's diamonds was close to 0.12±0.01 pMC, well above that of the lab's background of purified natural gas (0.08 pMC).

2. The ^{14}C was produced by U-fission (actually it's *cluster decay* of radium isotopes that are in the uranium decay chain). This was an excuse proposed for ^{14}C in coal, also analysed in Dr Baumgardner's paper, but not possible for diamonds. But to explain the observed ^{14}C, then the coal would have to contain 99% uranium, so colloquial parlance would term the sample 'uranium' rather than 'coal'.[8]

3. The ^{14}C was produced by neutron capture by ^{14}N impurities in the diamonds.

   But this would generate less than one ten-thousandth of the measured amount even in best case scenarios of normal decay. And as Dr Paul Giem points out:

   One can hypothesize that neutrons were once much more plentiful than they are now, and that is why there is so much carbon-14 in our experimental samples. But the number of neutrons required must be over a million times more than those found today, for at least 6,000 years; and every 5,730 years that we put the neutron shower back doubles the number of neutrons required. Every time we halve the duration of the neutron shower we roughly double its required intensity. Eventually the problem becomes insurmountable. In addition, since nitrogen creates carbon-14 from neutrons 110,000 times more easily than does carbon-13, a sample with 0.000 0091% nitrogen should have twice the carbon-14 content of a sample without any nitrogen. If neutron capture is a significant source of carbon-14 in a given sample, radiocarbon dates should vary wildly with the nitrogen content of the sample. I know of no such data. Perhaps this effect should be looked for by anyone seriously proposing that significant quantities of carbon-14 were produced by nuclear synthesis *in situ*.[9]

   Also, if atmospheric contamination were responsible, the entire carbon content would have to be exchanged every million years or so. But if this were occurring, we would expect huge variations in radiocarbon dates with porosity and thickness, which would also render the method useless.[1] Dr Baumgardner thus first thought that the ^{14}C must have been there right from the beginning. But if nuclear decay were accelerated, say a recent episode of 500 million years worth, it could explain some of the observed amounts. Indeed, his RATE colleagues have shown good evidence for accelerated decay in the past, which would invalidate radiometric dating.

4. The ^{14}C 'dates' for the diamonds of 55,700 years were still much older than the biblical timescale. This misses the point: we are not claiming that this 'date' is the actual age; rather, if the earth were just a million years old, let alone 4.6 billion years old, there should be no ^{14}C at all! Another point is that the 55,700 years is based on an assumed ^{14}C level in the atmosphere. Since no one, creationist or evolutionist, thinks there has been an exchange of carbon in the diamond with the atmosphere, using the standard formula for ^{14}C dating to work out the age of a diamond is meaningless. Also, ^{14}C dating assumes that the $^{14}C/C$ ratio has been constant. But the Flood must have buried huge numbers of carbon-containing living creatures, and some of them likely formed today's coal, oil, natural gas and some of today's fossil-containing limestone. Studies of the ancient biosphere indicate that there was several hundred times as much carbon in the past, so the $^{14}C/C$ ratio would have been several hundred times smaller. This would explain the observed small amounts of ^{14}C found in 'old' samples that were likely buried in the Flood.

amonds

reationist's best friend

Article from
Creation **29**(2):12–15
March 2007

Did God create life

Otherwise why is the universe so big?

Gary Bates

MANY PEOPLE, Christian or otherwise, struggle with the notion that the earth is the only inhabited planet in this enormous universe. In short, is there life on other planets?

Those who believe life evolved on the earth usually see it as virtual 'fact' that life has evolved on countless other planets. Discovering life on other planets would in turn be seen as confirming their evolutionary belief.

But even many Christians think, 'God must have created life elsewhere, otherwise this enormous universe would be an awful waste of space.' In my experience, this seems to be the major underlying reason why people think that there must be other life 'out there'. However,

our thinking should be based on what God said He did (the Bible), and not what we think He would, should or might have done.

Firstly, since God is the one who made the universe, it can scarcely be 'big' to Him. Our comprehension of size is limited to the created time/space dimensions within which we exist, and it is mind-bending to try and comprehend anything beyond our dimensional existence. And size and time are related somewhat. Because the universe is big to us we consider how long it would take us to travel across it, for example. But, time itself began with the creation of the physical universe, so how can we comprehend what eternity is, or might be? What was 'before' the universe? Similarly, how do we imagine how 'big' God is? We cannot use a tape measure that is made of the very atoms He made to

measure Him. One example of this might be if you were asked to build a small house and you did. Now you are asked to build a large house. In our dimensions, for you to build the larger house it would require more effort and take more time. So, is it harder, or does it take longer for God to build a big universe compared to a smaller one (according to our perspective on what constitutes large or small of course)? Of course not, because He isn't bound by time and space (which He created). Isaiah 40:28 says, "The Lord is the everlasting God, the Creator of the ends of the earth. He does not faint or grow weary; ...". If God is omnipresent, it does not take Him any 'time' to travel across the universe. He is 'here and there' simultaneously.

We are impressed that God made billions of galaxies with billions of stars in them and suitably so, because that is

on other planets?

one of the reasons for making them. But as mentioned, size is not an issue for God. Stars are relatively simple structures as they are just great big balls of gas. It would take more 'creative input', in that sense, for Jesus' miracle of feeding the five thousand than for the creation of countless quasars (there is immense genetic complexity in the structure of even a dead fish).

The Bible and ETs

It is often asked, 'Just because the Bible teaches about God creating intelligent life only on Earth, why *couldn't* He have done so elsewhere?' After all, Scripture does not discuss everything, e.g. motor-cars. However, the biblical objection to ET is not merely an argument from silence. Motor cars, for example, are not a salvation issue, but we believe that sentient, intelligent, moral-decision-capable beings is, because it would undermine the authority of Scripture. In short, understanding the big picture of the Bible/gospel message allows us to conclude clearly that the reason the Bible doesn't mention extraterrestrials (ETs) is that there aren't any.[1] Surely, if the earth were to be favoured with a visitation by real extraterrestrials from a galaxy far, far away, then one would reasonably expect the Bible, and God in His sovereignty and foreknowledge, to mention such a momentous occasion, because it would clearly redefine man's place in the universe.

1.   The Bible indicates that the *whole creation* groans and travails under the weight of sin (Romans 8:18–22). The effect of the Curse following Adam's Fall was *universal*.[2] Otherwise what would be the point of God destroying this *whole creation* to make way for a new heavens and Earth—2 Peter 3:13, Revelation 21:1 ff? Therefore, any ETs living elsewhere would have been (unjustly) affected by the Adamic Curse through no fault of their own—they would not have inherited Adam's sin nature.

2.   When Christ (God) appeared in the flesh, He came to Earth not only to redeem mankind but eventually the *whole creation* back to Himself (Romans 8:21, Colossians 1:20). However, Christ's atoning death at Calvary cannot save these hypothetical ETs, because one needs to be a physical descendant of Adam for Christ to be our "kinsman-redeemer" (Isaiah 59:20). Jesus was called "the last Adam" because there was a real first man, Adam (1 Corinthians 15:22,45)—not a first Vulcan, Klingon etc. This is so a sinless

73

human Substitute takes on the punishment all humans deserve for sin (Isaiah 53:6,10; Matthew 20:28; 1 John 2:2, 4:10), with no need to atone for any (non-existent) sin of his own (Hebrews 7:27).

3. Since this would mean that any ETs would be lost for eternity when this present creation is destroyed in a fervent heat (2 Peter 3:10, 12), some have wondered whether Christ's sacrifice might be repeated elsewhere for other beings. However, Christ died *once for all* (Romans 6:10, 1 Peter 3:18) on the *earth*. He is not going to be crucified and resurrected again on other planets (Hebrews 9:26). This is confirmed by the fact that the redeemed (earthly) church is known as Christ's bride (Ephesians 5:22–33; Revelation 19:7–9) in a marriage that will last for eternity.[3] Christ is *not* going to be a polygamist with many other brides from other planets.

4. The Bible makes no provision for God to redeem any other species, any more than to redeem fallen angels (Hebrews 2:16).

Fitting them in there ... somehow!

It should also be remembered that expressions like "the heavens and earth" (Genesis 1:1) are a figure of speech known as a *merism*. This occurs when two opposites or extremes are combined to represent the whole or the sum of its parts. For example, if I said "I painted the whole building from top to bottom." One would understand this to mean everything in the whole building. Similarly, biblical Hebrew has no word for 'the universe' and can at best say 'the all', so instead it used the merism "the heavens and the earth". New Testament passages like the aforementioned Romans 8:18–22 and Hebrews 11:3 clearly point back to the Genesis ("heavens and earth") creation, and thus, everything that God made and when time as we know it began.

Another is the passage in John 10:16 in which Jesus says, "And I have other sheep that are not of this fold. I must bring them also, and they will listen to my voice. So there will be one flock, one shepherd." However, even an ET-believing astronomer at the Vatican (thus a 'hostile witness' to the 'no ETs cause'), a Jesuit priest by the name of Guy Consalmagno, concedes, "In context, these 'other sheep' are presumably a reference to the Gentiles, not extraterrestrials."[4] Jesus' teaching was causing division among the Jews (vs. 19), because they always believed that salvation from God was for them alone

Jesus was reaffirming that He would be the Saviour of *all* mankind.

A novel approach

A more recent idea to allow for ETs arose out of a perceived need to protect Christianity in the event of a real alien visitation to Earth. Michael S. Heiser is an influential Christian UFOlogist/speaker with a Ph.D. in Hebrew Bible and Ancient Semitic Languages. He claims that the arguments put forward earlier might not apply to God-created aliens. Because they are not descendants of Adam they have not inherited his sin nature, and thus, are not morally guilty before God. Just like 'bunny rabbits' on the earth, they do not need salvation—even though they will die, they are going to neither heaven nor hell.

On the surface this seems a compelling argument; after all, fallen angels are intelligent but are beyond salvation ("For surely it is not angels that he helps, but he helps the offspring of Abraham" Hebrews 2:16). Angels are immortal and not of our corporeal dimension. And Heiser's ETs in spaceships require a level of intelligence not found in rabbits. This acutely highlights the injustice of their suffering the effects of the Curse, including death and ultimately extinction when the heavens

Could there be 'simple life' elsewhere in space?

The Bible's 'big picture' seems to preclude *intelligent* life elsewhere in God's universe[1] (see main text). But what about bacteria on other planets for example? It's possible that God made these, but exceedingly unlikely.[2] What would be their purpose? The entire focus of creation is mankind on this Earth; the living forms on Earth's beautifully balanced biosphere are part of our created life support system.

If bacteria are found elsewhere in the solar system, it will be hailed as proof that life can 'just evolve'.[3] However, we have previously predicted in print that in such an unlikely event, the organisms will have earth-type DNA, etc., consistent with having originated from here as contaminants—either carried by recent man-made probes, or riding fragments of rock blasted from Earth by meteorite impacts.

References

1. Bates, G., *Alien Intrusion: UFOs and the evolution connection*, Creation Book Publishers, Powder Springs, USA, 2010, and our documentary *Alien Intrusion: Unmasking a Deception*; alienintrusion.com.
2. Sarfati, J., Conclusive evidence for life from Mars? Remember last time! creation.com/mars, 15 May 2002.
3. Matthews, M., Space life? Answering unearthly allegations, *Creation* 25(3):54–55, 2003; creation.com/space_life.

vanish "like a scroll that is being rolled up" (Revelation 6:14). It also seems bizarre to assign no moral responsibility for the actions of highly intelligent beings.

The Bible says we are made in God's image *and* likeness (Genesis 1:26). Man was immediately created a fully intelligent being about 6,000 years ago and was involved in craftsmanship shortly thereafter (Genesis 4:22). Since that time, even we have not been able to develop technologies advanced enough to travel to other star systems. If aliens were capable of developing incredible faster-than-light spaceships needed to get here, one would presume they must have been created

Two identical Mars Rovers traverse the surface searching for evidence of water. Evolutionary researchers are eagerly looking for past or present signs of (even) microscopic life.

with vastly superior intellect to ours—which would make them even more in God's likeness in that sense than we are. Or, their creation is much older than the 6,000 years of the biblical six-day time-frame; the aliens were created before man and had sufficient time to develop their technologies. However, God created Earth on Day 1 and later the heavenly bodies on Day 4.

Influenced from outside the Bible

Although Heiser does not promote theistic evolution, he is sympathetic to a universe billions of years old (with its huge theological problems, as explained in "Did God create over billions of years?", p. 8). In theory, this could allow the time necessary for any unseen ETs to develop the almost science-fiction-like technologies required to get here. But, this is circular reasoning.

Ranking the created order

Psalm 8:5 says that man was made "a little lower than the angels and crowned with glory and honour". Heiser has said that salvation is based upon ranking, not intelligence. If so, where in the Bible (which omits to mention them) would ET sit in this pecking order? Would they be higher than man, and lower than angels, for example? If these advanced ETs were capable of visiting the earth, mankind would now be subject to *their* dominion. (Even if the ETs were friendly, potentially they would be much more powerful due to their intelligence and technology.) This would be in direct contravention to God's

ordained authority structure when he ordered mankind to 'subdue' the earth—also known as the dominion mandate (Genesis 1:28).

Be 'awe' inspired

Psalm 19:1 tells us a major reason that the universe is so vast: 'The heavens declare the glory of God; and the firmament shows His handiwork.' There are many similar passages in Scripture. They help us understand who God is and how powerful He is.

It reminds us that the more we discover about this incredible universe, the more we should be in awe of the One who made it all. In short, rather than looking up and wondering, 'I wonder what else is out there?' and imaginary aliens we've never seen, we should instead be considering the very One that made it all. ∎

References and notes

1. Of course, there are angelic beings. These were made early in Creation Week—referred to as 'sons of God' and 'morning stars' in the poetry of the book of Job, they rejoiced and sang at the formation of the earth's 'foundations' (Job 38:7).
2. Sarfati, J., The Fall: a cosmic catastrophe: Hugh Ross's blunders on plant death in the Bible, *J. Creation* **19**(3):60–64, 2005; creation.com/plant-death.
3. The church was bought with the blood of its Saviour from the wound in His side, a clear analogy to the first woman being born from a 'wound' in Adam's side.
4. Consolgmagno, G., Humans are not God's only intelligent works, 3 January 2006. He actually took the affirmative side in a debate with CMI's Dr Jonathan Sarfati (they didn't see each other's arguments before publication in the liberal *Science and Theology News*).

- **Top:** *Apatosaurus excelsus*
- **Bottom:** *Diplodocus carnegii*

The skulls above are from two huge sauropods with different names. Yet the skulls are almost identical. Thus they are likely from the same Diplodocid kind. Diplodocus was a very long and slender variety (27 m long, but only 10 tonnes), while Apatosaurus was a slightly shorter but much heavier variety (25 m, 35 tonnes). So, while there are many dinosaur names, there were most likely comparatively few created kinds. This means that Noah's Ark needed comparatively few pairs of dinosaurs.

Photos: Don Batten

GROW SO BIG?

IT THEM ON THE ARK?

■ Jonathan Sarfati

DINOSAURS FASCINATE kids of all ages, not least because of their immense size, many far bigger than the largest land animals living today.

What about the huge ones? Were they simply old?

Until fairly recently, scientists thought that the dinosaurs could grow so big because they were reptiles. Reptiles can keep growing till they die, while mammals (including man) stop growing at adulthood. According to the *Encyclopædia Britannica CD* (2005):

The significant difference between growth in reptiles and that in mammals is *that a reptile has the potential of growing throughout its life*, whereas a mammal reaches a terminal size and grows no more, even though it may subsequently live many years in ideal conditions [italics added].

The pro-evolution *Walking with Dinosaurs* website provided an example of this reasoning:

A huge animal called *Seismosaurus* was found in New Mexico and many palaeontologists believe it is really an old *Diplodocus*. It weighed 30 tonnes and was 45 metres (150 ft) long.[1]

And the *Walking with Dinosaurs* TV series itself claimed that the huge size

(150 tonnes) they claimed for the pliosaur *Liopleurodon* meant it must have been over 100 years old.

Dinosaur Growth Spurts

But this couldn't explain everything. There's no way a gecko or skink, for example, will grow as big as a 50-tonne *Brachiosaurus*. Gregory Erickson, a paleontologist at Florida State University in Tallahassee, and other researchers studied dinosaur bones for their equivalent of growth rings.[2] They showed that dinosaurs had a type of adolescent growth spurt—the pattern is called sigmoidal, or s–shaped. In fact, the growth pattern is more similar to that of birds and mammals than that of reptiles.[3]

For example, in the huge *Apatosaurus*, the spurt started at the age of about five years, when the dinosaur was only one tonne. During the spurt, it grew at over five tonnes per year, then the growth levelled off at the age of 12–13, when it was about 25 tonnes (see graph, above right). This was the most dramatic example, but other dinosaurs such as the 1700 kg (3700 lb) *Maiasaura* and the much smaller 20 kg (44 lb) *Syntarsus* and *Psittacosaurus* had the same sigmoid pattern.

Article from
Creation **28**(1)
January 2006

DINOSAUR SIZES

It's not easy to decide the biggest dinosaur, because some candidates have very fragmentary remains. E.g. *Amphicoelius fragillimus*, claimed to be 60 m (200 feet) long and weighing 122 tonnes, is known from a single huge vertebra 2.6 m (8.5 feet) tall, which is now *lost*. The "largest dinosaur known from a majority of the skeleton" is *Futalognkosaurus dukei*: 30 m (100 feet) long and over 50 tonnes;[1] its pelvis (hip bone) was 3m (10 feet) across.

There were some smaller dinosaurs that were only the size of roosters, but the smallest mammals, lizards, amphibians, and birds are much smaller than roosters. Combining all known dinosaurs, average size of a mature dinosaur was 630 kg (1389 lb), or the size of an American bison ('buffalo'), although most were either much smaller or much larger than that.[2]

BABY DINOSAURS GIVEN DIFFERENT NAMES

Also, dinosaurs are now known to undergo significant shape changes while growing. So many named dinosaurs were really juvenile versions of other named dinosaurs.[3] For example, Nanotyrannus was probably a juvenile *T. rex*; and the very young *Dracorex hogwartsia* grew into first the older juvenile *Stygimoloch spinifer* then into the adult *Pachycephalosaurus wyomingensis*;[4] and the *Torosaurus* may be an old *Triceratops*.[5] This is more proof that dinosaur discoverers are often too quick to assign new names, and that Noah required even fewer dinosaur pairs on the Ark.[6]

References and notes

1. Paul, G.S., *The Princeton Field Guide to Dinosaurs*, p. 233, 2nd Edn, Princeton University Press, 2016.
2. Clarey, T. and Tomkins, J.P., Determining average dinosaur size using the most recent comprehensive body mass data set, *Answers Research Journal*, 18 February 2015.
3. Handwerk, B., A third of dinosaur species never existed?, *National Geographic News*, news.nationalgeographic.com, 9 October 2009.
4. Williamson, T. and 3 others, Early ontogeny of pachycephalosaurine squamosals as revealed by juvenile specimens from the Hell Creek Formation, eastern Montana, *J. Vertebrate Paleontology* **29**(1):291–294, 2009.
5. Scannella, J. and Horner, J.R., *Torosaurus* Marsh, 1891, is *Triceratops* Marsh, 1889 (Ceratopsidae: Chasmosaurinae): synonymy through ontogeny, *J Vertebrate Paleontology* **30**(4):1157–1168, 2010 | doi:10.1080/02724634.2010.483632.
6. Catchpoole, D., Dino 'puberty blues' for paleontologists, creation.com/dino-puberty-blues, 15 June 2010

Erickson later led a distinguished team in a study just of the tyrannosaurid kind, including the mighty *T. rex*. This showed the same pattern. At the age of 10, it was still less than half a tonne. But after it started its growth spurt, from age 14–18 it grew at a rate of about 2 kg (4–5 pounds) per day, or a maximum of 767 kg per year. By its early 20s, it was about as big as it would ever be, they said—about 5½ tonnes.[4] However, the biggest specimen, the famous 'Sue', was also the oldest, but they still estimated that it was only 28 when it died (full of injuries[5]).

Erickson said, "*T. rex* lived fast and died young. They were like the James Dean of dinosaurs."[6]

This study also analyzed other tyrannosaurids called *Daspletosaurus*, *Gorgosaurus* and *Albertosaurus*. These all had the same growth patterns, but not nearly as extreme. So it seems that they were the same created kind, and *T. rex* was simply a giant form, just as we have

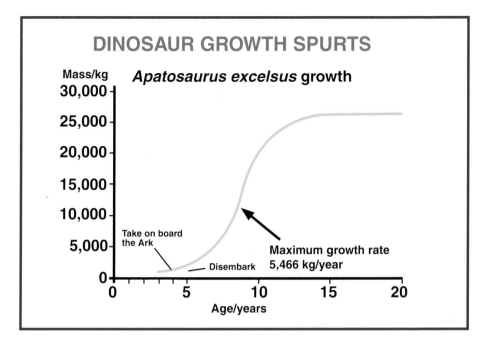

DINOSAUR GROWTH SPURTS

Apatosaurus excelsus growth

Mass/kg

Take on board the Ark

Disembark

Maximum growth rate 5,466 kg/year

Age/years

In all, although there are an estimated 668 dinosaur 'species', it's more likely that there were only about 55 created kinds with lots of varieties within these kinds.[10]

Summary

Noah would have been able to take all the dinosaur kinds on board the Ark because:

- Most dinosaur kinds were small.
- Even the big dinosaurs were small before their teenage growth spurt.
- There were comparatively few real kinds of dinosaur compared to the number of named 'species'.

References and notes

1. Walking with Dinosaurs Dino fact file: *Diplodocus*, abc.net.au/dinosaurs/fact_files/scrub/diplodocus.htm, 25 August 2004.
2. For example, there are lines of arrested growth (LAGs) when bones stopped or slowed growing. Also, fast-growing bone has a characteristic fibrolamellar texture, where fibres are quickly deposited, and leave holes that are filled with bony structures called osteons. Conversely, slow-growing bone has a lamellar-zonal structure, which is finely layered. See Stokstad, E., Dinosaurs under the knife, *Science* **306**(5698):962–965, 5 November 2004.
3. Erickson, G. *et al.*, Dinosaurian growth patterns and rapid avian growth rates, *Nature* **412**(6845):429–433, 26 July 2001.
4. Erickson, G.M. *et al.*, Gigantism and comparative life-history parameters of tyrannosaurid dinosaurs, *Nature* **430**(7001):772–775, 12 August 2004.
5. Sarfati, J., 'Sue', the *T. rex*: Does it show that dinosaurs evolved into birds? *Creation* **22**(4):18–19, 2000; creation.com/t-rex-wishbone.
6. Gosline, A., Bone rings hold the secrets to dinosaurs' enormous size, *New Scientist* **183**(2460):8, 2004.
7. *T. Rex* was a lumbering old slow coach, *New Scientist* **173**(2332):6, 2 March 2002.
8. *T. Rex*: The bigger they are, the slower they go, *Creation* **24**(3):56, 2002; creation.com/t-rex-slow.
9. Morton, M.C., Teen pregnancy in dinosaurs a good thing, *Geotimes*, January 2008.
10. Sarfati, J., *Refuting Compromise*, chs. 7–8, Master Books, Arkansas, USA, 2004.

JONATHAN SARFATI, B.Sc.(Hons.), Ph.D., F.M.

Dr Sarfati's Ph.D. in physical chemistry is from Victoria University, Wellington, NZ. He is the author of the best-selling Refuting Evolution 1 *and* 2 *and* Refuting Compromise. *A former NZ chess champion, he works full-time for* Creation Ministries *in Atlanta.*

in some humans. And as with many giant humans, the giantism comes at a cost.

Superficially, the *T. rex* body plan might give the impression it was a fast runner. But this structure simply will not allow fast running for this type of animal over one tonne, which the *T. rex* reached at age 13. So the Jurassic Park scene of a *T. rex* outrunning a jeep is pure fiction—to do that, it would have needed muscle weighing over twice the entire animal![7,8]

Noah's Ark cargo—not a problem!

Bibliosceptics frequently mock the account of Noah and the Ark by asking, 'How could Noah round up all the huge dinosaurs?' Of course, this is a leading question—Noah didn't have to round up anything, because God sent the animals to him (Genesis 6:20).

Certainly, dinosaurs would have been on the Ark: God told Noah to take two of every kind of land animal (seven of the few 'clean' animals). Dinosaurs were land animals, and they must have been alive then, because so many of them were fossilized in the Flood.

But these studies show, once again, that it's rash to claim that the Bible is wrong based on current data. The sceptic can never be sure that no new data won't refute the claim of biblical error. These studies suggest a means of fitting the animals on board. God could well have chosen specimens He knew would undergo their growth spurt as soon as they left the Ark. This would solve the common skeptical problem of fitting and feeding huge dinosaurs on the Ark. That is, they weren't actually that huge while they were on board. The growth spurt just after the Ark would also mean that they could quickly outgrow predators.

Furthermore, female dinosaurs have been discovered to have *medullary tissue* in their bones—this lines bone marrow and keeps them from losing calcium from their bones when they use it to make egg shells. This tissue has been found in dinosaurs that were not fully grown. It follows that dinosaurs didn't need to be fully grown before they could reproduce.[9]

And the tyrannosaurid study suggests that a *T. rex* pair was not required. Rather, another pair, not affected by gigantism, could have represented this created kind. This applies to all the dinosaurs. *Diplodocus* and *Apatosaurus* have virtually identical skulls (see photos, p. 76), so it's possible that the former was a very long and slender variant and the latter, a shorter, but much more massive, variety. And this diplodocid kind included the huge *Seismosaurus*, as mentioned above.

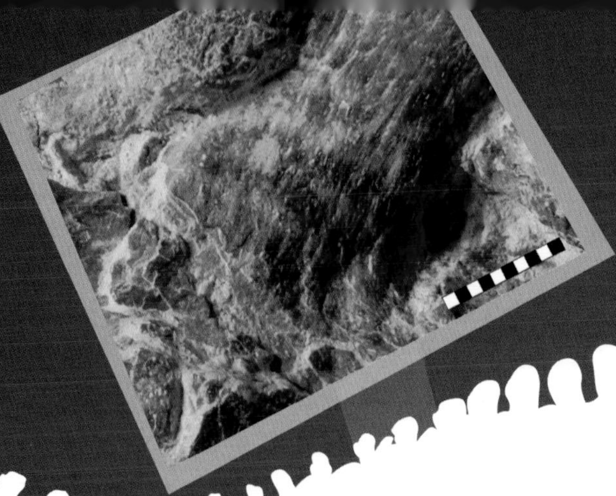

ORIGINAL ANIMAL PROTEIN IN

FOSSILS?

YES!

DINOSAURS, MARINE REPTILES,
PTERODACTYLS, BIRDS, INSECTS,
LIZARDS, FROGS, SALAMANDERS,
MAMMALS, SQUID, FISH

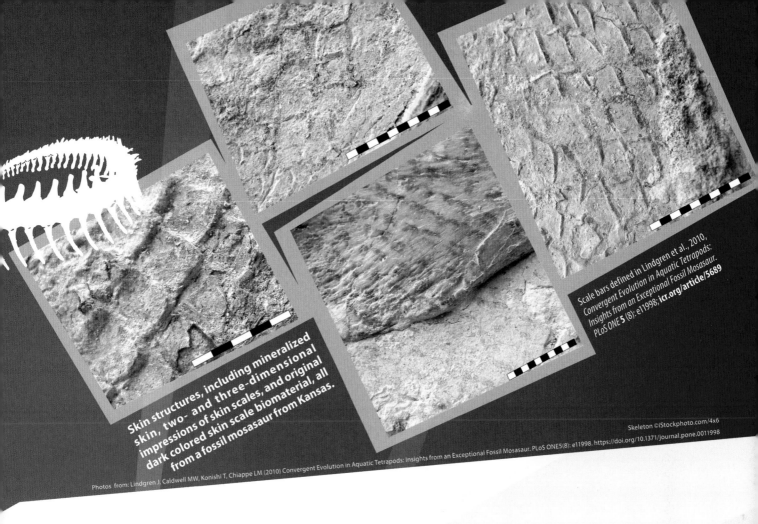

Skin structures, including mineralized skin, two- and three-dimensional impressions of skin scales, and original dark colored skin scale biomaterial, all from a fossil mosasaur from Kansas.

Scale bars defined in Lindgren et al., 2010, *Convergent Evolution in Aquatic Tetrapods: Insights from an Exceptional Fossil Mosasaur.* PLoS ONE 5 (8): e11998: icr.org/article/5689

Skeleton ©iStockphoto.com/4x6

Photos from: Lindgren J, Caldwell MW, Konishi T, Chiappe LM (2010) Convergent Evolution in Aquatic Tetrapods: Insights from an Exceptional Fossil Mosasaur. PLoS ONE5(8): e11998. https://doi.org/10.1371/journal.pone.0011998

■ Brian Thomas

I FIRST learned about original soft tissue fossils from *Creation* magazine in 1997.[1] What looked like red blood cells and blood vessels from inside *Tyrannosaurus* bone did not fit what I had been told about how fossils are millions of years old. I immediately understood that the fossil, and therefore the rock layer that held it, could be no older than thousands of years.

At that time, wise scientists warned that further investigations could either invalidate or validate the outrageous find. Now, many discoveries in special pockets around the world have validated many such original animal tissue fossils.

Sometimes 'soft tissue' fossils refer to impressions in rock that preserve an animal body outline, like squid, algae, or worm bodies, or of dinosaur skin or footprints. Scientists may also refer to tissue replacement by minerals like phosphate, pyrite, or carbon as 'soft tissue preservation.' Stable substances like rocks and minerals can last a very long time, but not so the animal's original biochemicals.

Reliable techniques have detected chitin, chitin-associated protein, elastin, fibrin, osteocalcin, keratin, hemoglobin, DNA, and collagen, and many other such proteins in various fossils. Comparing the degree of wholeness of the fossil biochemicals to the same biochemicals from modern animal tissue reveals that the fossil material has only *partly* decayed. Those biochemicals should have *completely* decayed over any claimed period of millions of years into tiny molecules like carbon dioxide, water, or ammonia. But paleontologists keep finding original biochemistry—like finding mummified remains—encased in rock.

Take collagen, for example. It is a resilient, strand-like protein molecule that strengthens hard mineral in bones and sea (mollusc) shells, and strengthens skin and connective tissue. Collagen's toughness explains why skin, and thus parchment, is long-lasting. But parchment does not last for even half of a million years. We know this from examining the Dead Sea Scroll parchments. After two millennia, they are quickly turning to dust.

In fact, we know from calculations based on straightforward scientific principles that collagen *could* last hundreds of thousands of years, and we know that it *could not* last multiple millions of years. In 2011, UK archaeologists and experts on bone collagen decay wrote that "it will take between 0.2 and 0.7 Ma [million years] at 10°C for levels of collagen to fall to 1% in an optimal burial environment."[2] So, collagen could last 450,000 or so years on average. If kept below freezing, it might be imagined to last one or two million years *at the very most*. But evolutionists agree that dinosaurs lived in a very warm climate, so in their scenario, this would vastly shrink the times—at 20°C, collagen would have decomposed below the detection limit in about 15,000 years.[3,4]

However, I have found many reports of collagen-containing

Article from
Creation 35(1):14–16
January 2013

DOES OTHER EVIDENCE CONFIRM THOUSANDS OF YEARS?

Those who insist that dinosaur and other fossils are millions of years old often cite radioisotope dates. Although radioisotopes appear to have undergone millions of years' worth of decay at today's slow rates, other data shows that those rates were dramatically accelerated in the past. First, rocks of known historical age always yield vastly inflated radioisotope ages.[1] Also, the helium leakage age of granites is only six thousand years.[2,3] Third, all carbon-containing Earth materials so far tested, including diamond, contain abundant radiocarbon, a tell-tale signature of material that is no more than about 50 thousand years old.[4] So their radioisotope ages are all wrong.

Scientists plan to obtain radiocarbon ages of dinosaur bone. In the meantime, a 2011 study reported a radiocarbon age for a fossil mosasaur [marine reptile] bone of 24,600 years.[5] Of course, the fossil could be even younger. Age estimates based on radiocarbon decay and based on tissue decay agree on a maximum age range of thousands of years.

Using natural processes such as these for age-dating always requires assumptions. In contrast, the Bible is a collection of reliable eyewitness accounts co-authored by the Creator. It holds straightforward age information, including a tight time range for Noah's Flood, which occurred around 4300 years ago.

Most of the fossils with original soft tissues were deposited by the waters of that same Flood retreating off of continents about 4300 years ago, consistent with the observation that the tissues have not yet completely decayed.

1. See articles under "Are there examples of inaccurate results obtained from the potassium/ argon dating method?" at creation.com/dating.
2. See creation.com/RATE which references the major articles of the ICR-sponsored RATE research group's breakthrough.
3. Humphreys, D. R., A Tale of Two Hourglasses, *Acts & Facts* **35**(12), 2006; icr.org/article/ tale-two-hourglasses.
4. Giem, P., Carbon-14 Content of Fossil Carbon. *Origins* **51**: 6–30, 2001; grisda.org/ origins/51006.htm. See also creation.com/diamonds.
5. Lindgren, J. *et al.*, Microspectroscopic Evidence of Cretaceous Bone Proteins. *PLoS ONE* **6** (4): e194 45, 2011.

fossils designated as *tens* of millions of years old. Some fossils even have skin or cartilage collagen, which is not encased in protective bone or shell mineral. A number of these reports are listed on a chart published online at the Institute for Creation Research website.[5] But I am always finding more.

In the chart, I listed a *T. rex* collagen protein sequence described in 2005. Collagen fibres from a *Psittacosaurus* dinosaur were published in 2008. The most thoroughly analyzed original soft tissue fossil so far is the 2009 hadrosaur femur. It was from Hell Creek Formation in Montana, the same formation as the *T. rex* found in 2005. The hadrosaur's blood vessels had plenty of original collagen. I even found a report of original dinosaur bone collagen that was found in the Gobi desert in 1966.[6]

We have a fine fossil fish with original collagen fibres featured on an office wall at ICR (see photo top right). It is from the Green River Formation in Wyoming. How do we know it is actually original fish collagen? First, it is a different colour, hardness, and texture from the surrounding rock. One visitor said that it looks like beef jerky. Second, the paleontologists who prepared it wrote that it was collagen. To dispel any doubt, scientists used four independent techniques to directly test fossil lizard skin from the same formation as our fish.[7] They wrote,

"Taken together, all the analyses performed in this study strongly suggest that the fossilized reptile skin in

BHI- 102B [the lizard fossil] is not a simple impression, mineralized replacement or an amorphous organic carbon film, but contains a partial remnant of the living organism's original chemistry, in this case derived from proteinaceous skin."[8]

Although collagen cannot last longer than hundreds of thousands of years at realistic temperatures, it is right there in a supposedly 50 million-year-old lizard leg, and a supposedly 50 million-year-old fossil fish. And the dinosaur collagen fossils are supposed to be even older! Clearly, their age assignments are not correct (see inset). Original soft tissue fossils appear to be thousands of years old because that is their actual age range, just as biblical history indicates. ■

References and notes

1. Wieland, C., Sensational dinosaur blood report! *Creation* **19**(4):42–43; creation. com/ dino_blood, 1997.
2. Buckley, M. and Collins, M., Collagen survival and its use for species identification in Holocene-lower Pleistocene bone fragments from British archaeological and paleontological sites. *Antiqua* **1**(e1):1–7, 20 September 2011 | doi:10.4081/antiqua.2011.e1.
3. Nielsen-Marsh, C., Biomolecules in fossil remains: Multidisciplinary approach to endurance, *The Biochemist* **24**(3):12–14, June 2002; biochemist.org/ bio/02403/0012/024030012.pdf.
4. Doyle, S., The Real Jurassic Park, *Creation* **30**(3):12–15, 2008; creation.com/real-jurassic-park.
5. Published Reports of Original Soft Tissue Fossils, *Institute for Creation Research*, icr. org/soft-tissue-list. See also creation.com/ double-decade-dinosaur-disquiet.
6. Pawlicki, R., Corbel, and H. Kubiak, H., Cells, collagen fibrils, and vessels in dinosaur bone. *Nature* **211**(5049):655–657, 1966.
7. See Thomas, B., Green River Formation Fossil Has Original Soft Tissue. *ICR News*; icr.org/article/green-river-formation-fossil-has-original, 12 May 2011.
8. Edwards, N.P. *et al.*, Infrared mapping resolves soft tissue preservation in 50 million year-old reptile skin, *Proceedings of the Royal Society B.* **278**(1722):3209–18, 2011.

BRIAN THOMAS, M.S.
Brian is a science writer at the Institute for Creation Research *in Dallas, Texas, contributing to ICR's website and print publications.* Creation *magazine was instrumental in moving Brian from evolution to creation.*

Article from
Creation **10**(4):38
September 1988

Carl Wieland

SNAKES DO EAT DUST!

IN GENESIS 3:14 we read, "The Lord God said to the serpent, '… on your belly you shall go, and dust you shall eat all the days of your life.'" Micah 7:17 says, "they [the nations] shall lick the dust like a serpent."

Since snakes do not really appear to eat dust, this has been taken as an example of either obvious metaphor (which seems reasonable) or an example of the Bible's propensity to error, depending upon one's bias. As an example of the former, Herbert Carl Leupold (1891–1972), a conservative Lutheran who was Professor of Old Testament Exegesis in the Capital University Seminary, Colombus, Ohio, points out that "eating dust":

> … in every case implies 'to be humbled', 'to suffer defeat'. So in addition to a humiliating manner or mode of locomotion there will be a continual suffering of defeat 'all the day' of her existence. The serpent will always be a creature that is worsted.[1]

However, once more we have the situation where, as more information has come to light, the Bible has been shown to be not only accurate, but accurate in minute detail. Snakes do deliberately and purposely eat and lick dust.

There is an organ in the roof of a snake's mouth called *Jacobson's organ* or *vomeronasal organ* (VNO). Like the sense of smell, it is a system designed to detect many different kinds of chemicals. But the VNO specializes in non-volatile chemicals, so requires direct physical contact. Its darting, forked tongue samples bits of dust by picking them up on the points of the fork, which it then presents to its matching pair of sensory organs inside its mouth. Once it has 'smelt' them in this way, the tongue must be cleaned so the process can be repeated immediately.

Therefore serpents really *do* lick dust and eat it. ∎

References and notes

1. Leupold, H.C., *Exposition of Genesis* **1**:162, 1942.

Beetle bloopers

Flightless insects on windswept islands
Even a defect can be an advantage sometimes

Carl Wieland

A BIG obstacle for evolutionary belief is this: what mechanism could possibly have added all the extra information required to transform a one-celled creature progressively into pelicans, palm trees, and people? Natural selection alone can't do it—selection involves getting rid of information. A group of creatures might become more adapted to the cold, for example, by the elimination of those which don't carry enough of the genetic information to make thick fur. But that doesn't explain the origin of the information to make thick fur.

For evolutionists there is only 'one game in town' to explain the new information which their theory requires—mutations. These are accidental mistakes as the genetic information (the coded set of instructions on the DNA which is the 'recipe' or 'blue-print' specifying the construction and operation of any

creature) is copied from one generation to the next. Naturally, such scrambling of information will tend to either be harmful, or at best neutral. (See box, p. 85, and "The 3 Rs of Evolution", p. 99)

However, evolutionists believe that occasionally, a 'good' mutation will occur which will be favored by selection and will allow that creature to progress along its evolutionary pathway to something completely different.

The wrong type of change

Are there 'good' mutations? Evolutionists can point to a small handful of cases in which a mutation has helped a creature to survive better than those without it. Actually, they need to take a closer look. Such 'good' mistakes are still the wrong types of changes to turn a fish into a philosopher—they are headed in precisely the *wrong direction*. Rather than adding information, they *destroy* information, or *corrupt* the way it can be

expressed (not surprising, since they are random mistakes).

For example, beetles losing their wings. A particular winged beetle type lives on large continental areas; the same beetle type on a small windy island has no wings.

What happened is easy to imagine. Every now and then in beetle populations, there might be a mutational defect which prevents wings from forming. That is, the 'wing-making' information is lost or scrambled in some way.

The damaged gene (a gene is like a long 'sentence' carrying one part of the total instructions recorded on the DNA) will then be passed to all that beetle's offspring, and to theirs, as it is copied over and over. All these descendant beetles will be wingless.

If a beetle with such a wingless defect is living on the Australian mainland, for example, it will have less chance to fly away from beetle-eaters, so it will be more likely to be eliminated by 'survival

84

Mutations and degeneration

As expected from copying mistakes, mutations are often harmful. Thousands of hereditary diseases in people, for instance, are caused by just such inherited mutational defects. Certainly loss of flight and loss of sight is still a loss, even if it can be beneficial, or helping the organism to survive. Similarly, eyeless fish in pitch-black caves might even have an advantage because they will not get infected eyes, and natural selection would not eliminate sightlessness when sight is irrelevant.[1]

A neutral mutation is one that has no effect on the outcome, or the expressed meaning of the code. Using English as an (admittedly limited) analogy, assume a message were transmitted saying 'the enemy is now attacking', which accidentally suffers a one-letter substitution changing it to 'the enemy is not attacking'. The result is potentially disastrous, like a harmful mutation. Whereas a change to 'tha enemy is now attacking' would be neutral; a change, but not affecting the end result.

However, because the downhill change of 'the' to 'tha' would not have a big enough effect for natural selection to work on, there would be nothing to stop their accumulation. Eventually, enough of these small changes would accumulate so they do real damage, analogous to the gibberish statement: 'tha eneme it no artackong'. This is an example of 'genetic entropy' that would lead to extinction over long-age time scales.[2]

1. Wieland, C., Let the blind see … Breeding blind fish with blind fish restores sight, *Creation* **30**(4):54–55, 2008; creation.com/blindsee.
2. Plant geneticist: 'Darwinian evolution is impossible': Don Batten chats with plant geneticist John Sanford, *Creation* **30**(4):45–47, 2008, creation.com/sanford.

of the fittest' before it can leave offspring. Such *natural selection* can help to eliminate (or at least reduce the buildup of) such genetic mistakes.

Blown away

However, on the windy island, the beetles which can fly tend to get blown into the sea, so not having wings is an advantage. In time, the elimination of all the winged ones will ensure that only those of this new 'wingless' variety survive, which have therefore been 'naturally selected'.[1] 'There!' says the evolutionist. 'A favorable mutation—evolution in action!' However, it fails to make his case, because though beneficial to survival, it is still a *defect*— a loss or corruption of information. This is the very *opposite* of what evolutionists need to demonstrate real evolution.

To support belief in a process which has allegedly turned molecules into man would require mutations to *add* information. Showing that information-losing defects can give a survival advantage is irrelevant, as far as evidence for real evolution is concerned.

In short,

1. Evolutionary theory requires some mutations to go 'uphill'—to add information.
2. The mutations which we observe are generally neutral (they don't change the information, or the 'meaning' in the code) or else they are informationally downhill—defects which lose/corrupt information.
3. The rare 'beneficial' mutations to which evolutionists cling, all appear to be like this wingless beetle—downhill changes, losses of information which, though they may give a survival advantage, are headed in precisely the wrong direction for evolution.

All of our real-world experience, especially in the 'information age', would indicate that to rely on accidental copying mistakes to generate real information is the stuff of wishful thinking by 'true believers', not science. ■

References and notes

1 Darwin himself invoked wingless beetles in the exposed Desertas islands of the Madeira archipelago off the coast of Morocco as an example of natural selection of a beneficial loss of function (*Origin of Species*, 'Use and Disuse', ch. V, 1859). As shown, we agree!

Article from
Creation **19**(3):30
December 1997

Broken Images

FOR CHRISTIANS WHO BELIEVE GOD USED EVOLUTION, THE IMAGE OF GOD ISSUE IS A SERIOUS PROBLEM FOR THEIR IDEAS

■ Lita Cosner

"SO GOD created man in His own image, in the image of God created He him; male and female created He them" (Genesis 1:27, KJV). This important and well-known passage of Scripture provides our understanding of who we are as human beings.

What is the image of God?

Man alone, both male and female, is created in the image of God, and this is the basis for our special relationship with Him. It's different to that of animals, who do not have eternal spirits; and angels, who are not offered salvation if they sin (Hebrews 2:16). But what exactly does being created in the image and likeness of God mean?

Theology professor Wayne Grudem writes:

"When God says, 'Let us make man in our image, after our likeness' (Gen 1:26), the meaning is that God plans to make a creature similar to himself. Both the Hebrew word for 'image' (*tselem*) and the Hebrew word for 'likeness' (*demût*) refer to something that is *similar* but not identical to the thing it represents or is an 'image' of."[1]

God created mankind to be like Him in certain ways and to represent Him. Some try to find a specific characteristic that primarily reflects the image of God, such as language or intellectual capacity. But we should not limit God to a certain few characteristics, since the Bible never does so.

Unfallen man reflected the image of God in that he was endowed with all the communicable attributes of God, such as the capacity for discernment, wisdom, love, holiness, etc. There are attributes of God such as His omnipresence, self-sufficiency, omnipotence, and omniscience that He could not give to His creations because they are uniquely part of God's nature.

The unfallen image

Before the Fall, Adam and Eve were as much like God as limited physical beings could be; they were the pinnacle of God's creation. To be in a perfect relationship with God, they needed to have the appropriate attributes for that. They were created sinless—corrupted flesh could not live face to face with God. They were endowed with moral choices, and had authority over the earth as God's stewards (Genesis 1:28). They were able to perfectly obey or to disobey God's commands, and be accountable for those choices. Beyond this, there is no biblical evidence that Adam's pre-Fall abilities were much different to those of humans today, despite some believing that he may have had supernatural control over the Creation, like God.

At the Incarnation, Jesus Christ, the Son of God, also displayed the perfect image of God the Father. The Bible describes Him as "the image of the invisible God" (Colossians 1:15) and as "the exact representation of His being" (Hebrews 1:3). He not only had the *capacity* to perfectly obey God's law,

but being sinless He *did* do so, which is important to our understanding of how we can therefore be saved through Him.

God's image: the basis for Satan's hatred

We don't know a lot about Satan's pre-Fall history, but the biblical data enable us to constrain the timing of his Fall. Sometime between God's declaration that everything He made was "very good" on Day Six, and Eve's temptation, Satan had already rebelled against God. By the time he came on the scene in Genesis 3 in the form of a serpent, he was already opposed to God, and tempted Eve to disobey God. The Bible clearly indicates that humans (the ones whom God loves—John 3:16) are especially the targets of Satan. This makes sense—he hates God and tried to usurp His role, but failed. But he can torment God's image bearers, and drag as many to Hell (which was created originally as a place of punishment for the fallen angels—Matthew 25:41) with him as possible.

Sin and the broken image

Adam and Eve's sin had disastrous consequences for them, for all their descendants, and for the whole universe. Because Adam was the corporate head of all of creation, all of creation fell. God's image bearers were now marred and would now die (Romans 5:12–19). Their souls would face the terrible fate of eternal conscious separation from Him (Matthew 25:41). They could no longer exercise dominion as effectively, because much of the fallen creation was now hostile to them (Genesis 3:17–19).

Some say that *no* part of the image of God remains, because a sinful image cannot be an image of God at all. However, this follows only if there is a direct one-to-one comparison between God and His image. Yet we know that there isn't, because His image-bearers

were always limited in ways that God is not.

Some important biblical passages teach that human beings remain in the image of God. First, to kill a human being is such a serious offense it carried a death penalty. Murder "betrays an attempt or desire (if one were able) to attack God himself,"[2] even if someone is not aware of that desire. In the Old Testament, even an animal had to be slaughtered if it killed a human (Exodus 21:28–32). James appeals to the likeness of God in 3:9 where he condemns the hypocritical behavior of blessing God and cursing human beings who have been made in the image of God. There are many other examples in Scripture.

The basis for salvation

Humans alone out of all creatures have the opportunity to repent and be restored into a right relationship with God. This is because only we are in God's image and thus have the capacity for redemption. Human beings, even only retaining a broken image, remain in the centre of God's plan for creation, and ever since the Fall, the goal of all of history has been the restoration of His people. We were so important to Him that He sent a rescue mission from Heaven by His Son becoming a man (John 1:14). But why did God take on the characteristics of a fallen creature?

Jesus' purpose was to redeem human beings (Philippians 2:7). So, he became our Kinsman Redeemer (Isaiah 59:20). The reason why the "image of the invisible God" could take on human form is that humans were also originally made in the image of God.

Salvation: the image partially restored

When we trust in Jesus for salvation, we are justified, or declared legally righteous before God (Romans 5:18–19), and we are indwelt with the Holy

Spirit (Romans 8:9,15; Galatians 4:6; Ephesians 1:13). As temples of the Holy Spirit, it reinforces the fact that we are still capable of being His image bearers. Then God begins the work of restoring His fuller image in us. This includes sanctifying us—the progressive work of bringing us into line with His standards (Philippians 2:13, Galatians 5:22–23). As we walk with the Lord in this life, we are brought more and more into alignment with His will, and even with pre-Fallen humanity.

But we still only bear a marred image of God—we still sin and fall short of what God intended for us (Romans 3:23). We also still die, but through death we can actually be restored to fellowship with our Creator via new sinless, glorified Resurrection bodies (1 Corinthians 15:42 ff.).

The New Earth and the image fully restored

The fallen state of God's image-bearers is an affront to God, and explains why there had to a human mediator (1 Timothy 2:5). His own glory demands that He restore a people for Himself, because the goal of creation was anthropocentric (man-centred), in that God desired to have a relationship with His image-bearers characterized by our freely-given love and loyalty. If God did not, or could not, redeem a 'bride', it would imply that Satan could thwart God's purposes. So God restores those who trust in Christ to show His supremacy.

The resurrection is *bodily*; we'll have physical bodies that are recognizably human, and they'll have some continuity with our current bodies, though without the defects and weaknesses that the Fall introduced. These bodies will never experience sickness, suffering, or death (Revelation 21:4), because sin was paid for by the blood of the Lamb—the mediator Jesus Christ.

Morally, we'll be perfectly sinless too; we won't have the slightest desire or capability to sin—like Christ. Our nature will desire to obey God completely as we will no longer war against the desires of the flesh. It will be thus even better than in Eden. There *will* be no potential to sin again. Sin *will* be defeated once and for all, and our natures will be completely conformed to His image.

The image of God— an evolved ape?

For Christians who believe God used evolution, the image of God issue is a serious problem for their ideas. The doctrine of man in God's image is linked with the doctrines of creation and restoration. If we're just advanced apes who are descended from the same single-celled organism as everything else, then there's no basis for claiming we're special. Will God restore us to ape-like creatures? Man had to be a direct supernatural creation of God in order for us to bear His image.

Conclusion

Like most doctrines, one has to look at the whole Bible, from Genesis to Revelation, to understand the doctrine of the image of God and how it affects us. A faulty understanding of the Genesis foundation will necessarily affect how we see the image of God in the rest of Scripture. ■

References and notes

1. Wayne Grudem, *Systematic Theology*, p. 442, Grand Rapids: Zondervan, 1994.
2. Grudem, p. 444.

Article from
Creation **34**(4):46–48
October 2012

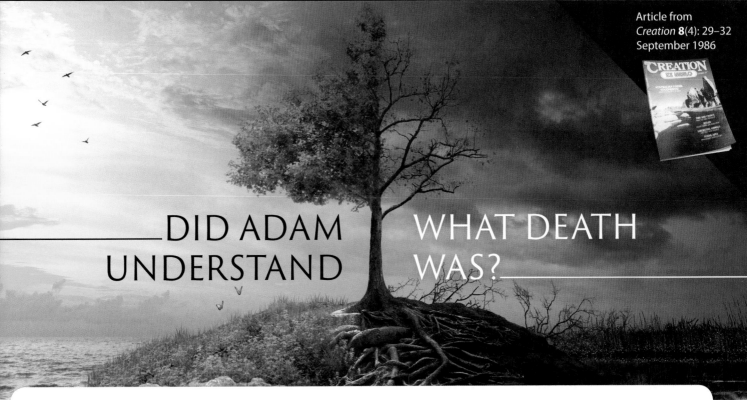

Article from
Creation **8**(4): 29–32
September 1986

DID ADAM UNDERSTAND WHAT DEATH WAS?

Charles Taylor

A THEOLOGIAN who didn't want to accept that death entered the world through Adam (Romans 5:12; 1 Corinthians 15:22) posed the question, "How could Adam know what death meant if he'd never seen death before?" He was saying that God's warning in Genesis 2:17 would have meant nothing to Adam if Adam didn't know what death meant because he hadn't experienced it personally or seen it in operation.

Let's consider what Adam could or couldn't understand.

First, God declares that His creation is perfect, and that Adam is made in the image of God. The usual understanding of this statement is that since God had a will, Adam had one also, one which Adam could use whether it was in his interests or not. Like God, Adam had the capacity to love, to be unselfish. He was different from the animals for animals are not like this. They may appear at times to display something like love, but experiments demonstrate that, in similar circumstances, they always react in the same way—by instinct. Thus an animal cannot be truly selfish or unselfish, but operates on a programmed behaviour pattern.

In Genesis 2:19 we read that Adam was commanded to name the animals. He'd never done this before, but he obviously both understood the command and

succeeded without problems. God not only had implanted language in him, but also the ability to understand language. He was like God, made in God's image. Naming animals was a 'first', but Adam could do it. And Adam also understood new terminology which applied to things he had not seen or done before. Adam had to know what 'trees' were (Genesis 2:16), what 'plants' were, what 'eat' meant, and what 'fruit' was, and so on.

Each one of those events was a first, yet Adam had no problems with them. Why not? Because Adam was made as the reflection of the God who calls Himself the Word (John 1:1–18). So it is only to be expected that communication skills figured highly among Adam's newly created talents.

Man's freedom to choose makes him unique. In biblical terms, man was created good in every sense, but also had a capacity to reject good or to sin, though he need not have sinned. Included in 'good' is 'intelligent', since Adam was made in the image of the all-knowing God. To assume that he could not understand everything God said to him is therefore folly. Even a child today (though vastly inferior in intellect to the freshly created Adam) can gain a quick understanding of new things. Even in our own life growth to adulthood, there always has to be a first time for every new concept and we come to understand it. Adam would easily have understood what God was talking about.

Even if we assume Adam did not fully understand death, he would realize death was neither good nor in his best interests since he was told about it in a warning against the due consequences of failing to follow God's instructions. It is even possible that God used tone of voice or something else to convey to Adam the danger of the situation. The same as any parent does to warn a child of a danger the parent doesn't want the child to learn by experience. To doubt Adam's understanding is to claim that the Creator God has only a limited ability to communicate.

In modern language studies, linguists have shown that a child's ability to understand language precedes a child's ability to express in language by a fairly appreciable time factor. It is quite obvious that children understand their parents' intentions long before they can reply to their parents' questions or formulate questions to them.

The God who could take dust and make a man could easily empower a perfectly made Adam to understand the messages he was speaking to him. ■

Charles V. Taylor (1918–2009), M.A., Ph.D., PGCE, LRAM, FIL, Cert. Theol.
Dr Taylor earned B.A.s in languages, music and theology, an M.A. in applied linguistics and a Ph.D. in a central African language. He was a Fellow of the Institute of Linguists, and for eight years served as coordinator of applied linguistics courses at The University of Sydney. The author of nine Christian books, he served on the staff of Garden City School of Ministries and on the Board of Creation Science Foundation (later Creation Ministries International–Australia*). For more:* creation.com/charles-v-taylor.

HANGING

Carl Wieland

ONE OF the most common caricatures made of creation science is that, because it begins with the Bible, it has nothing to do with investigative science. Science asks questions, they say, then looks for answers. So if you start with answers, how can you be doing science?

However, we are obviously not claiming that God has revealed all possible knowledge in His Word. We do claim, though, that where He *has* clearly revealed certain facts relating to reality (science, history) these are true as opposed to untrue. This has nothing to do, incidentally, with 'wooden-headed literalism', 'bibliolatry' or a 'failure to appreciate the nature of the literature'.

Creation magazine and creation.com have already published evidence that virtually all top Hebrew-language scholars at world-class universities (even, perhaps especially, the nonbelievers among them) understand that the *meaning* of Genesis (i.e. as the original readers would have understood it) is to give us a simple yet factual account of the origins and history of man and the universe, just as is obvious to any straightforward reading by even a child. Thus, holding to recent fiat creation in six earth-days, a globe-covering Flood, etc., is not some peculiar invention of any twentieth century movement but inevitably results from an honest, scholarly dealing with the text itself.

But such matters merely give us the outline, the corner-posts as it were, for a framework of understanding within which to interpret and correlate the facts of the real world. They do *not* give us all the answers. Rather, they prevent us wasting time looking in the wrong direction while trying to establish the details of the fascinating subjects of the history of man and his world.

'Aha!', say the anticreationists, 'You see? They admit that their investigation is limited by their biblical framework. Evolution-science is open-minded and objectively searching for the truth.' **Not so**. There are rigid rules in evolution-science

CURRENT CREATIONIST THINKING

This article has long been regarded as sound advice, so if a particular *model* can be discarded as new evidence comes in, without being a threat to the direct biblical teaching. For example, most creationists abandoned the canopy theory around the turn of the millennium, and many now think that catastrophic plate tectonics is the best. But this too still a model on which to 'hang loose'.[1]

Creationists also reject the 'snap freeze of woolly mammoths'; rather they were buried by gigantic dust storms near the close of the post-Flood ice age—and frozen quickly but not in a 'snap'.[2] The moon dust argument should not be used any more, because earlier evolutionists had over-estimated the amount of incoming dust.[3]

We also advise against the 'shrinking sun' argument, because neutrino evidence shows that the sun is shining by fusion not gravitational collapse. But because fusion should shrink the core, the reactions should become more intense, and the sun should become more luminous with age. So billions of years ago, it should have been much fainter, and the earth would have been totally covered by ice—yet there is no evidence for this. Not a problem for a 'young' earth.[4]

1. Batten, D. (ed.), *Creation Answers Book*, chapters 10–12, CBP, 2014.
2. Oard, M., Woolly mammoths were cold adapted, *J. Creation* **28**(3):15–17, 2014; creation.com/mammoths-cold.
3. Snelling, A. and Rush, D., Moon dust and the age of the solar system, *J. Creation* **7**(1):2–42, 1993.
4. Sarfati, J., Our steady sun: a problem for billions of years, *Creation* **26**(3):52–53, 2004; creation.com/faint-sun.

Pavel Chernobrivets/123RF

90

LOOSE

too. You may open-mindedly discuss and consider all possible mechanisms of evolution, but you are only allowed to contemplate explanations which conclude that matter is responsible for its own order and complexity—that is, that there has never been any supernatural creation (compare "A Tale of two fleas", p. 50). And in all of this, we must remember that origin-science of whatever flavour is inherently different from operation science (how the universe *presently* works—gravity, physics, chemistry, etc.) because we can't directly test or observe stories about the past.

Because of these sorts of misunderstandings, it is vital that we consider carefully which are the fundamentals of the biblical origins framework. The clear, unmistakable issues on which honesty demands no compromise (e.g. global Flood) must be carefully separated from those issues which are a 'secondary construct', and on which we must be prepared to 'hang loose', if necessary.

For instance, the venerable pre-Flood vapour canopy model. This is an excellent concept which appears to be implied in the Bible and answers a lot of problems. But it is not and never can be regarded as a direct teaching of Scripture.

In the heady and fascinating search for the best explanation in such areas of origin-science as the mechanisms of the 'mammoth deep-freeze', for example, let us always hold our ideas lightly, in a tentative fashion. Is the sun shrinking? What about the moon dust? New evidence is always coming in—sometimes this will strengthen an existing idea, sometimes it will have to be abandoned (see Box p. 90 for current thinking). Similarly, evolutionists have been forced to abandon nearly all the evidences which were used in the earlier part of this century to condition generations of schoolchildren (useless leftover 'vestigial' organs, gill-slits in human embryos based on Haeckel's forged embryo diagrams, Neandertals as subhumans, 'Piltdown man', etc.).

Standing firm on the basics, yet holding lightly to secondary theories and models as the years go by will prevent Bible-believing Christians having anywhere near as much egg on their faces in this area as the disciples of Darwin have had to endure.

Article from
Creation **11**(2):4
March 1989

GEOLOGY
AND THE YOUNG EARTH

ANSWERING THOSE BIBLE-BELIEVING BIBLIOSKEPTICS

THERE ARE THESE PROBLEMS

Tas Walker

THE HAND-WRITTEN note pinned to some photocopied pages was typical. "I wonder if you could help with a geological problem?" The writer, who identified himself as a Bible-believing Christian, was confused. He had just encountered some tired old geological arguments attacking the straightforward biblical account of earth history—i.e., denying a recent creation and a global Flood on the basis of 'geological evidences'.

A number of books in the last 25 years have stirred up these so-called 'geological problems' and undermined faith in the Bible for many people. Sadly, the ones which cause most confusion and distress are those written by professing 'Bible-believers'.[1]

A curriculum writer with a Christian home school association wrote to us that he was "pretty well wiped out" after reading these books.[2] He wondered if we "might have answers to what these gentlemen say." We certainly have! Another person who had read some of them said, "I may have been … overlooking information that cast doubts upon the recent creation model."

Because the "recent creation model" is really what the Bible plainly says (see "Should Genesis be taken literally?", p. 108), he has really been caused to doubt the Bible.

The unsuspecting readers of such books, thinking they are getting something from 'Bible-believing Christians', expect encouragement and faith-building material. They are generally unprepared for the explosive mixture of heretical theology, poor science and vehement attacks on Bible-believers.

For example, the author Alan Hayward claims to be a 'Bible-believing Christian' [he died in 2008, years after this article was published—Ed.]. However, he is a Christadephian, which means he denies the tri-unity of God and the deity of Christ, clearly taught throughout the New Testament (see "Is Jesus Christ the Creator God?", p. 34). Clearly, 'Bible-believing' Hayward chooses to reinterpret those parts of the New Testament with which he disagrees.

He worked the same way with the Old Testament. Instead of accepting the clear teaching of Genesis, he reinterpreted the passages to fit his billion-year preference for the age of the earth.

In so doing, of course, he introduces confusion and problems that destabilize readers. We are warned to beware of teachers who vandalize the clear teaching of Scripture to fit with their philosophy (Colossians 2:8).

Superficially, Hayward amasses an impressive battery of arguments as to why the Bible can't mean what it says. Perhaps the single most important lesson from his book is his strategy itself. Each of his attacks on the Word of God elevates some other 'authority', whether derived from geology, astronomy, secular history or theology, above the Bible. This approach is as old as the Garden of Eden (Genesis 3:1–5).

True knowledge begins with the Bible (Proverbs 1:7, Psalms 119:160; 138:2), and that is where we need to start. God was there when He created the world. He knows everything, does not tell lies, and does not make mistakes. It is from the Bible that we learn that the world is 'young' (see also "How does the Bible teach 6,000 years?", p. 28).

If the Bible taught that the world was millions of years old,[3] we would believe that. However, the concept of millions of years of death and suffering contradicts the Word of God, and destroys the foundation of the Gospel of Christ (see also "What should a Christian think about evolution?", p. 12).

Many people find it difficult to accept that scientific investigation should start with the Bible. They think we can answer the question about the age of the earth by coming to the evidence with an 'open mind'. In fact, no one has an open mind. Evidence does not interpret itself; rather, everyone views the world through a belief framework. Unfortunately, as humans we never have all the information. So, when we start from the evidence, we can never be sure our conclusions are right—like in a classic 'whodunnit', just one piece of information can change the whole picture. By contrast, when we start from the Word of God, we can be sure that what it says is true.

Even if we can't answer some of the apparent problems now, we can be confident that there *is* an answer. We may not find out about the answer on this side of eternity, but that would simply be because we did not have all the information necessary to come to the right conclusion. On the other hand, ongoing research *may* reveal the answer—and it often has, as we will see.

On first appearance, the evidence that Hayward assembles seems so overwhelming. But the problems he describes are easily answered—indeed many answers were known before he wrote his book. Either he was unaware of the answers, or he deliberately ignored them. Let's look at some of the 'science' he presents so persuasively.

VARVES

A common argument against the Bible involves varves—rock formations with alternating layers of fine dark, and coarse light sediment. Annual changes are assumed to deposit bands with light layers in summer and dark layers in winter. It is reported that some rock formations contain hundreds of thousands of varves, thereby 'proving' the earth is much older than the Bible says.

But the assumption that each couplet always takes a year to form is wrong. Recent catastrophes show that violent events like the Flood described in Genesis can deposit banded rock formations very quickly. The Mount St Helens eruption in Washington State produced 8 m (25 feet) of finely layered sediment in a single afternoon![4] And a rapidly pumped sand slurry was observed to deposit about

a metre (3–4 feet) of fine layers on a beach over an area the size of a football field (cross-section shown on the right: normal silica sand grains are separated by darker layers of denser mineral grains like rutile).[5]

When sedimentation was studied in the laboratory, it was discovered that fine bands form automatically as the moving water transports differently sized particles sideways into position.[6] Surprisingly, the thickness of each band was found to depend on the relative particle sizes rather than on the flow conditions. A layered rock (diatomite) was separated into its particles, and when redeposited in flowing fluid, identical layers formed.

Much is often made of the Green River varves, in Wyoming, USA. But these bands cannot possibly be annual deposits because well-preserved fish and birds are found all through the sediments.

It is unthinkable that these dead animals could have rested on the bottom of the lake for decades, being slowly covered by sediment. Their presence indicates catastrophic burial. It is often claimed that the fish and birds remained in prime condition at the bottom of the lake because the water was highly alkaline and this preserved their carcasses. Yet, highly alkaline water causes organic material, including proteins and fats, to disintegrate, and that is why alkaline powder is used in dishwashers! Another problem for the varve explanation is that the number of bands is not consistent across the formation as it should be if they were annual deposits.[7]

Another claim of biblioskeptics is that there are 'too many fossils'. If all those animals could be resurrected, it is said, they would cover the entire planet to a depth of at least 0.5 metres (1.5 feet). So they could not have come from a single generation of living creatures buried by the Flood.[8]

Not surprisingly, the substance disappears when the detail is examined. The number of fossils is calculated from an abnormal situation—the Karroo formation in South Africa. In this formation, the fossils comprise a 'fossil graveyard'—the accumulation of animal remains in a local 'sedimentary basin'. It is certainly improper to apply this abnormally high population density to the whole earth.

Whether one concludes that sedimentary layers took millions of years of slow processes to form, or were the result of large catastrophic hydraulic forces, such as during and after the Genesis Flood, relates to the 'lenses of belief' through which the facts are interpreted.

Above: **Thin alternating bands in sedimentary rock like this have been used to argue for vast ages. But stratigraphic experiments show otherwise.**

Fossil 'graveyards' where the bones of thousands or even millions of animals were washed and then fossilised together, are wonderful evidence for the cataclysmic events associated with Noah's Flood.

The calculation also uses incorrect information on today's animal population densities and takes no account of the different conditions that likely applied before the Flood.[9]

The petrified forests of Yellowstone National Park have often been used to argue against Bible chronology. These were once interpreted as buried and petrified in place—as many as 50 successive times, with a brand new forest growing upon the debris of the previous one. Naturally, such an interpretation would require hundreds of thousands of years to deposit the whole sequence and is inconsistent with the Bible time-scale. But this interpretation is also inconsistent with the fact that the tree trunks and stumps have been broken off at their

FOSSIL FORESTS

base and do not have proper root systems. Furthermore, trees from different layers have the same 'signature' ring pattern, demonstrating that they all grew at the same time.

Rather than 50 successive forests, the geological evidence is more consistent with the trees having been uprooted from another place, and carried into position by catastrophic volcanic mudflows—similar to what happened during the Mount St Helens eruption in 1980, where waterlogged trees were also seen to float and sink with the root end pointing downwards.[10]

Conclusion

The box to the right shows some of the other arguments along this line that were once claimed to be 'unanswerable'. If this article had been written some years earlier, we would not have had all those answers. We still don't have all the answers to some others, but this does not mean that the answers don't exist, just that no-one has come up with them yet. There may be new arguments in the future alleging to 'prove' that the Bible, or one of the previous answers, is wrong. And when these are answered, there might be new

Divers examine a broken tree stump embedded upright on the bottom of Spirit Lake below Mt St Helens volcano. This stump was initially part of an immense floating log 'mat' and illustrates how the logs sank root end first.

ones again. That is the nature of science. All its conclusions are tentative, and new discoveries mean that old ideas must be changed—that is why creationist research is important. But science ultimately can't prove or disprove the Bible. Faith—but not a blind faith—is needed. It is not the facts that contradict the Bible, but the *interpretations* applied to them. Since we never will know everything, we must start with the sure Word of God in order to make sense of the world around us.

Upright fossilised trees in Yellowstone. Evidence shows they could not have grown in place.

References and notes

1 Hayward, A., *Creation and Evolution: The Facts and Fallacies*, Triangle, London, 1985.
2 Holzmann, J., Sonlight Curriculum, letter and catalogue on file; see also creation.com/hold-on-mr-holzmann.
3 The Hebrew writers could easily have described long ages if necessary—see Grigg R., How long were the days of Genesis 1? *Creation* **19**(1):23–25, 1996; creation.com/sixdays.
4 Walker, T., Learning the lessons of Mount St. Helens, *Creation* **39**(3):24–28, 2017.
5 Batten, D., Sandy stripes: Do many layers mean many years? *Creation* **19**(1):39–40, 1997; creation.com/sandy.
6 Julien, P., Lan, Y., and Berthault, G., Experiments on stratification of heterogeneous sand mixtures, *J. Creation* (1):37–50, 1994; creation.com/sandstrat.
7 Garner, P., Green River Blues, *Creation* **19**(3):18–19, 1997; creation.com/varves.
8 Creationists accept that some fossils formed post-Flood, but these are relatively few and do not alter the argument.
9 Woodmorappe, J., The Karoo vertebrate non-problem: 800 billion fossils or not? *J. Creation* **14**(2):47–49, 2000.
10 Sarfati, J., The Yellowstone petrified forests, *Creation* **21**(2):18–21, 1999; creation.com/yellowstone.
11 Snelling, A., Can Flood geology explain thick chalk beds? *J. Creation* **8**(1):11–15, 1994; creation.com/chalk.
12 Snelling, A.. and Woodmorappe, J., Granites—they didn't need millions of years of cooling, *Creation* **21**(1):42–44, 1998; creation.com/rapid-rocks.

More (former) problems more answers

Some similar geological problems which were once claimed to be 'unanswerable' for Bible-believers but for which there are now clear answers include:

- Chalk deposits need millions of years to accumulate. [Chalk accumulation is not steady state but highly episodic. Under cataclysmic Flood conditions, explosive blooms of tiny organisms like coccolithophores could produce the chalk beds in a short space of time.[11]]
- Granites need millions of years to cool. [Not when the cooling effects of circulating water are allowed for.[12]]
- Sediment kilometres thick covering metamorphic rocks took millions of years to erode. [Only at the erosion rates observed today. There is no problem eroding kilometres of sediment quickly with large volumes of fast-moving water during the Flood.]

Article from
Creation **21**(4):16–20
September 1999

CHEATING WITH CHANCE

Don Batten

THE ARGUMENT from probability that life could not form by natural processes but must have been created is sometimes acknowledged by evolutionists as a strong argument.[1] The probability of the chance formation of a hypothetical functional 'simple' cell, given all the ingredients, is acknowledged[2] to be worse than 1 in 10^{57800}. This is a chance of 1 in a number with 57,800 zeros. It would take 11 full pages of magazine type to print this number. To try to put this in perspective, there are about 10^{80} (a number with 80 zeros) atoms in the universe. Even if every atom in our universe were another universe the same size as ours that would 'only' amount to 10^{160} atoms.[3]

These numbers defy our ability to comprehend their size. Fred Hoyle, British mathematician and astronomer, used analogies to try to convey the immensity of the problem. For example, Hoyle said the probability of the formation of just *one* of the many proteins on which life depends is comparable to that of the solar system packed full of blind people randomly shuffling Rubik's cubes all arriving at the solution at the same time[4]—and this is the chance of getting only *one* of the more than 400 proteins needed for the simplest viable bacterial cell. As Hoyle pointed out, the program of the cell, encoded on the DNA, is also needed. In other words, life could not form by natural (random) processes.

Evolutionists often try to bluff their way out of this problem by using analogies to argue that improbable things happen every day, so why should the naturalistic origin of life be considered impossible? For example, they say the odds of winning the lottery are pretty remote, but someone wins it. Or, the chances of getting the particular arrangement of cards obtained by shuffling a deck is remote, but a rare combination happens every time the cards are shuffled. Or the arrangement of the sand grains in a pile of sand obtained by randomly pouring the sand is extremely complex, but this complex and improbable arrangement did occur as a result of random processes. Or the exact combination and arrangement of people walking across a busy city street is highly improbable, but such improbable arrangements happen all the time. So they argue from these analogies to try to dilute the force of this powerful argument for creation.

You probably realize there is something illogical about this line of argument. But what is it?

In all the analogies cited above, there has to be an outcome. Someone *must* win the lottery.[5] There *will* be an arrangement of cards. There *will* be a pile of sand. There *will* be people walking across the busy street. By contrast, in the processes by which life is supposed to have formed, there need not necessarily be an outcome. Indeed the probabilities argue against *any* outcome. That is the whole point of the argument. But then the evolutionist may counter that it did happen because we are here! This is circular reasoning at its worst.

Note several other things about these analogies:

- Creationists do not argue that life is merely complex, but that it is ordered in such a way as to *defy* a natural explanation. The order in the proteins and DNA of living things is independent of the properties of the chemicals of which they consist— unlike an ice crystal where the structure results from the properties of the water molecule. The order in living things parallels

Article from
Creation **17**(2):14–15
March 1995

that in printed books where the information is not contained in the ink, or even in the letters, but in the complex arrangement of letters which make up words, words which make up sentences, sentences which make up paragraphs, paragraphs which make up chapters and chapters which make up books. These components of written language respectively parallel the nucleic acid bases, codons, genes, operons, chromosomes and genomes which make up the genetic programs of living cells.

- The order in living things shows they are the product of intelligence. The result of the lottery draw is clearly the result of a random selection—unless family members of the lottery supervisor consistently win! Then we would conclude that the draw has not been random—it is not the result of a random process, but the result of an intelligent agent.

- The arrangement of cards resulting from shuffling would not normally suggest anything other than a random process. However, if all the cards were ordered by their suits from lowest to highest, we would logically conclude that an intelligent agent arranged them (or 'stacked the deck' in card-playing parlance) because such an arrangement is highly unlikely from genuine shuffling—a random, non-intelligent process.

- The arrangement of the sand grains in a pile would not normally suggest it resulted from intelligent activity rather than natural processes. However, if all the sand grains were lined up in single file, or were in a neat rectangle, we would attribute this to an intelligent agent, or a machine made by an intelligent agent, as this would not be likely from a natural process.

- The arrangement of people crossing a busy street would not normally suggest anything other than a random process. However, if all the people were ordered from shortest to tallest, or some other ordered arrangement, we would suspect that an intelligent agent was responsible for putting them in this order—that it did not result from chance. If 20 people were arranged from shortest to tallest, the odds of this happening by chance are less than one in a billion, billion (10^{18}), so it would be reasonable to conclude that such an ordered arrangement was not due to chance whereas there would be nothing to suggest intelligent involvement if there was no meaningful pattern to the arrangement of people.

Many scientists today claim that an invisible 'intelligent cause' is outside the realm of 'real' science. These scientists have redefined science as naturalism (nature is all there is). However, scientists recognize the evidence for an invisible intelligent agent when it suits them. For example, forensic science determines if past events were the result of accident or plan and purpose ('Who done it?'). The Piltdown ape-man fraud was discovered, after some 40 years, when researchers had the opportunity to examine the original bones and not just replicas, and they noticed file marks on the teeth.[6] Such marks do not happen by natural processes and the researchers recognized the involvement of a human (intelligent) agent—a hoaxer.

Likewise, United States taxpayers are spending millions of dollars yearly in funding the Search for Extra-terrestrial Intelligence (SETI). If those listening hear a radio signal with random noise, it is clearly the product of a natural process, but if there is a pattern such as 'dah-dah-dah-dit-dit-dit-dah-dah-dah', it will be hailed as evidence for an intelligent, although invisible, source.

If such evidence indicates an intelligent source then surely the incredible amount of information on the DNA in living things, equivalent to a library of a thousand Bible-sized books in every human cell,[7] *shouts creation by a Creator!* The more we know about the biochemical workings of living cells, the stronger the evidence becomes for the intimate involvement of a creator. We are indeed *fearfully and wonderfully made* and no amount of illogical and irrelevant analogy will counter the clear evidence for this. ■

References and notes

1. Bradbury, D.A., 'Reply to Landau and Landau', *Creation/Evolution* **13**(2):48–49, 1993.
2. Bradbury, Ref. 1.
3. Or, your credit cards have a 4-digit PIN, so one in 104 chance of getting it right, or perhaps three tries before the bank closes the card. The probability here is akin to a 57,800-digit PIN.
4. Hoyle, F., The big bang in astronomy, *New Scientist*, **92**(1280):527, 1981.
5. Even with lotteries where the prize jackpots if no-one gets the exact set of digits drawn, the number of digits to guess is adjusted in line with the number of tickets likely to be purchased to make sure that there will be a winner frequently and there are always lesser prizes for getting less than the full set of digits
6. M.L. Lubenow, *Bones of Contention—a Creationist Assessment of Human Fossils*, pp. 39–44, Baker Book House, Grand Rapids, 1992.
7. M. Denton, *Evolution: Theory in Crisis*, p.351, Burnett Books, London, 1985.

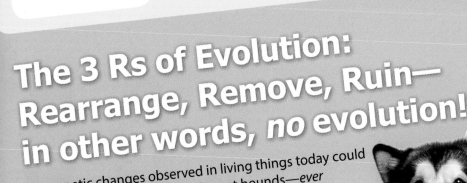

The 3 Rs of Evolution: Rearrange, Remove, Ruin— in other words, *no evolution!*

The genetic changes observed in living things today could not have turned bacteria into basset hounds—*ever*

■ **David Catchpoole**

EVOLUTION TEXTBOOKS cite variation as being something upon which 'evolution depends'.[1] However, when one examines closely the claimed 'demonstrable examples' of 'evolution', they actually fall into three categories, which we can label here as the '3 Rs'.

Let's look at each of these in turn.

'R'#1: Rearrange *existing genes*

Careful examination of many purported instances of 'evolution in action' shows that such 'variation' actually *already exists*, conferred by genes that *already exist*.

Here's a simplified example that shows this, and also how such genetic variety might be misconstrued as 'evidence of evolution'. The two dogs in the top row of Figure 1 are a male and a female. They each have a gene that codes for short hair (inherited from its mother or father) and a gene that codes for long hair (inherited from the other parent). In combination, this gene pair for fur length results in medium length hair.[2]

Now when these two dogs are crossed, what new combinations of the genes are possible in the resulting offspring? The second row of Figure 1 shows this:

- The dog at the far left has inherited its father's short-hair gene and its mother's short-hair gene. Result: short hair.
- The two dogs in the middle have each inherited a long-hair gene from one parent and a short-hair gene from the

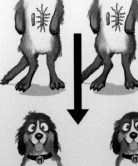

Figure 1. The red bars represent the genes for hair length (short and long hair). One of each gives medium length hair. By re-arranging (recombining) the parents' genes (top) in reproduction, variety is generated in the appearance of the offspring, but no new genes are involved.

other parent. Result: medium-length hair (just like the mother and father).

- The dog at the far right has inherited its mother's long-hair gene and its father's long-hair gene. Result: long hair.

A casual observer, looking only at the outward appearance, i.e. unaware of what is happening at the genetic level, might think: "There were no long-hair dogs in the parents' generation. This long hair is a new characteristic—evolution is true!"

But such a view is incorrect. The only thing this 'evolution' has done is to *rearrange existing genes*. There's simply been a sorting out of *pre-existing* genetic information. There's no new information here

of the kind needed to have turned pond scum into poodles, Pekingese, pointers and papillons.

'R'#2: Remove *genetic information*

What about natural selection, adaptation and speciation?

None of these represent the generation of any *new* microbes-to-mastiff genetic information either. In our 'hairy dog' example, if we were to send our new population of dogs, some with short hair, others with medium or long hair, to an icy, very cold location, we wouldn't be at all surprised to see natural selection at work, killing off any dog that didn't have long hair (Figure 2, Line 1). When the survivors reproduce, the only fur-length genes passed on to the offspring are those that code for long hair (Figure 2, Line 2).

Thus we now have a population of dogs beautifully *adapted* to its environment. Biologists encountering our ice-bound population of dogs, observing them to be isolated[3] from other populations of dogs, could argue that they be given a new *species* name.

So here we see *natural selection, adaptation, and possibly even speciation*—but *no new genes* have been added. In fact, there's been a *loss* of genes (the genetic information for short- and medium-length hair has been removed from the population).

Note that such examples of natural selection, adaptation and speciation are often portrayed as evidence for evolution, but the only thing this 'evolution' has done is to *remove* existing genes. If this population of exclusively long-hair dogs were now forcibly relocated to a steamy tropical island, the population could not 'adapt' to the hot climate unless someone re-introduced the short-hair gene to the population again, by 'back-crossing' a short- or medium-length hair dog from elsewhere. This is exactly the sort of thing that our crop and livestock breeders are doing. They are scouring the world for the original genes created during Creation Week[4] but which have subsequently been 'bred out' (lost) from our domestic varieties/breeds of plants and animals because of breeders artificially selecting certain characteristics, which means other features are de-selected (lost).

'R'#3: Ruin *genetic information*

In the above examples, we see that natural selection, adaptation and speciation are real and observable. And that these simply demonstrate the *rearranging* and/or *removing* of dog genes that were *originally present at Creation*. (I.e. by the end of Day 6, when God *completed* Creation, declaring it 'very good'—Genesis 1:31.)

However, there are forms of dog genes today which were *not* present at Creation but have arisen since. But those have not arisen by any *creative* process, but by *mutations*, which are copying mistakes (typos, we might say) as genes

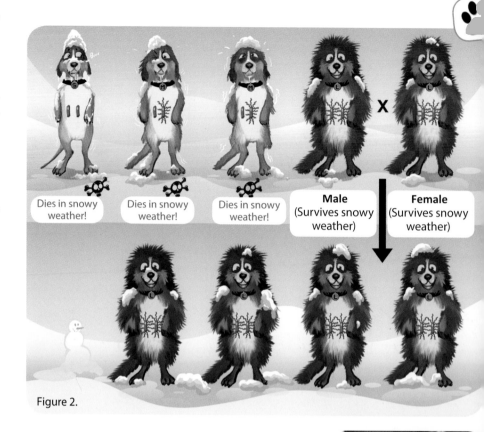

Figure 2.

Dies in snowy weather!

Dies in snowy weather!

Dies in snowy weather!

Male (Survives snowy weather)

Female (Survives snowy weather)

are passed from parents to offspring. You would expect such accidental changes to *wreck* the existing genes, and that's what happens. For example, the dog pictured in Figure 3 has just such a mutated gene, resulting in 'floppy ear syndrome'.[5]

Dogs with this genetic mutation have weaker cartilage and cannot lift up their ears. So they just hang, floppy before dinner, and sloppy after it—unless their owners are diligent in cleaning them. Such regular attention to ear hygiene is necessary, as dogs with floppy ears are prone to serious ear infections, which can even lead to hearing loss.[6] Not that their hearing was especially good anyway. As you might expect, dogs with erect ears are far superior to floppy-eared dogs at detecting prey by sound.[7]

I can remember reflecting on this when I was an atheist/evolutionist, and wondering how such floppy-eared dogs could have ever evolved and survived in the wild. I now know that they *didn't*. Instead this mutation in the genes has arisen since the original "very good" world (Genesis 1:31) was cursed as a result of Adam's sin (Genesis 3:17–19). The floppy-eared mutation in dogs is but one example of how a post-Fall world is very

Figure 3.

Figure 3: Dogs with the floppy ear mutation, such as bassets, are much more prone to ear infections (e.g. from food scraps) than dogs with erect ears (they clearly can't hear as well either!)

much "in bondage to decay" (Romans 8:19–22). So common is this mutational defect in modern domestic dogs that many people have naïvely come to think of floppy-eared dogs as 'normal'. But Adam and Eve, if they were alive today, would no doubt be shocked to see such deformity.

The original dogs, probably something like today's gray wolves, would have had *erect*, superbly functional, ears.

Why is this so important to consider, in the context of evolutionary claims that no Creator was necessary?

Evolutionary biologists, when pressed with the *facts* about natural selection, will concede that natural selection by itself can only remove existing genetic information. However, they argue that in tandem with mutations, natural selection would be a creative process.

But the floppy-ear mutation, for one, is a classic example of the widespread *degradation* of the genome—a *downhill* process. For microbes-to-man evolution to be true, evolutionists should be able to point to thousands of examples of information-gaining mutations, an *uphill* process, but they can't.[8] Mutations overwhelmingly *ruin* genetic information. Therefore evolutionists looking to mutations as being evolution's 'engine' do so in vain.[9] Thus they are left with no known mechanism capable of *ever* turning microbes into mutts—i.e. no way of 'climbing' up the supposed evolutionary 'tree'.

Note that while mutations degrade genetic information, sometimes an advantage arising from such degradation can outweigh the disadvantage vis-à-vis survival. While a floppy-eared mutant mutt might not last long in the wild, under human care—i.e. with regular ear cleaning—the equation changes. And what about the key moment when a buyer is looking for the 'cutest', friendliest pup in the pet shop window? Indeed, there is increasing evidence that the floppy-eared characteristic is strowngly associated with tameness.[10,11] Little wonder then, that floppy-eared dogs are so common today.[12]

Conclusion: 3 Rs = no new information = no evolution

The above examples of changes in fur length and ear structure of dogs are not evolutionary changes, though they are often claimed as such. *R*earranging genes, *R*emoving genes, and *R*uining genes are not the sort of genetic changes that could have turned bacteria into basset hounds— *ever*. These '3 Rs' are repeatedly cited as evolution in a host of other settings, too, e.g. in antibiotic and pesticide resistance,

and in sticklebacks, beetles, mosquitoes, worms, sheep, and codfish.[13] But none of these are evidence of evolution. The '3 Rs' could never add up to mosquitoes, mesquite, mutts, and man from microbes (let alone from molecules!).

The evidence instead fits with the biblical account of God having created a multiplicity of 'kinds', each programmed to reproduce according to its kind. Geneticists recognize that the diversity of dog breeds we have today could have arisen *quickly*, in recent history.[14] As we've seen in our fur length example, long hair and short hair can appear in *just one generation*, arising from the in-built canine genetic variation—variation that was built-in to dogs at Creation. So Noah didn't need to take on board the Ark multiple pairs of dingoes, Dalmatians, and dachshunds; or coyotes, corgis, and cocker spaniels; or jackals, jack russells, and jackadoodles. He only needed *two* dogs—just as the Bible suggests (Genesis 6:19–20). ∎

References and notes

1. E.g. page 32 of Pringle, L., *Billions of years, amazing changes: The story of evolution*, Boyds Mills Press, USA, 2011. For a comprehensive page-by-page rebuttal of the claims in that book see creation.com/pringle-review.
2. 'Co-dominant genes' would behave in this manner. The exact genetic basis of hair length is not known yet, but it is something like this, although there could be more than one pair of genes involved.
3. Geographic isolation is often used as a basis for a new species to be named. This is consistent with the somewhat arbitrary nature of species names, cf. the biblical 'kind'.
4. See Batten, D., What! … no potatoes? *Creation* **21**(1):12–14, 1998; creation.com/potatoes. Not all breeders would realize that this is in fact what they are doing. Sadly, they would pay homage to evolution rather than God.
5. Boyko, A. *et al.* Geneticists have now tracked the difference between floppy and erect ears to a single gene region in canine chromosome 10 (CFA 10). A simple genetic architecture underlies morphological variation in dogs, *PLoS Biology* **8**(8):e1000451, 2010.
6. Lougee, M., How to clean a dog's floppy and smelly ears, ehow.com, acc. 17 February 2017.
7. The selecting of hounds with floppy ears is understandable considering they have to rely more on smell and thus this sense is heightened; hence they tend to be good sniffer dogs (bloodhounds, etc.).
8. As information is foundationally an argument from probability, we might expect a few cases of trivial information increase (see our new DVD *Understanding the Law of Decay*, and creation.com/edge-evolution). But

evolution requires *encyclopedic* amounts of new information (lots of *new genes*). A lead candidate, nylon-eating bacteria, turns out not to be an example of a brand-new gene, as had been claimed. Rather, the new 'ability' comes from two 'typos' in an *existing* gene for an enzyme finely-tuned to break bonds in certain chemicals. The mutated enzyme is less tuned for its current task, but can digest *other* chemicals, including nylon, with the same bond (creation.com/evoquest#nylonase, creation.com/infoloss). See also Carter, R., Can mutations create new information? *J. Creation* **25**(2):92–98, 2011; creation.com/new-info.
9. Williams, A., Evolution's engine becomes evolution's end! *Journal of Creation* **22**(2):60–66, 2008; creation.com/evolutions-end.
10. Adams, J., Genetics of dog breeding, *Nature Education* **1**(1), 2008; nature.com.
11. Trut, L., Early canid domestication: the farm-fox experiment, *American Scientist* **87**:160–169, 1999.
12. For more see Cosner, L., 'Parade of mutants'— pedigree dogs and artificial selection, *Creation* **32**(3):28–32, 2010; creation.com/pedigree.
13. See creation.com/superbugs, creation.com/pesticide, creation.com/stickleback, creation.com/beetle, creation.com/brisk, creation.com/cadmium-worms, creation.com/bighorn, creation.com/tomcod, creation.com/smaller-fish.
14. Ratliff, E., How to build a dog—Scientists have found the secret recipe behind the spectacular variety of dog shapes and sizes, and it could help unravel the complexity of human genetic disease, ngm.nationalgeographic.com, February 2012.

**DAVID CATCHPOOLE,
B.Ag.Sc.(Hons.), Ph.D.**
Dr Catchpoole has worked as a plant physiologist and science educator, specializing in tropical agriculture and horticulture. He works full-time for Creation Ministries International in Australia.

Article from *Creation* **35**(2):47–49 April 2013

DOMINIC STATHAM

THERE ARE many similar plants and animals found in eastern Asia and eastern North America, but not in the regions between them (fig. 1). These include arachnids, millipedes, wasps, freshwater fish, and over 150 different seed plants.[1,2] Evolutionists try to explain this by saying that, many millions of years ago, the northern regions were warmer and eastern Asia and eastern North America were part of one continuous plant and animal distribution (fig. 2). Then, they say, around five million years ago, the climate cooled and the plant and animal life were separated (fig. 1).[3]

Some plants and fungi found in eastern Asia and eastern North America are so similar that they are classified as being the same species.[4,5] Others have been assigned different species names but probably should not have been. For example, the Snake Mouth Orchid is named *Pogonia ophioglossoides* when found in eastern North America, and *Pogonia japonica* when found in eastern Asia (fig. 3). When grown under the same conditions, however, they appear indistinguishable (fig. 4).

The Sacred Lotus (eastern Asia) and Yellow Lotus (eastern North America) are classified as two different species, *Nelumbo nucifera* and *Nelumbo lutea* (fig. 5).[6] However, their hybrid form is fertile, again indicating that they are really the same species.[7]

Figure 1. There are many similarities between the wildlife of eastern Asia and eastern North America.

Figure 2. Similar and identical species found in eastern Asia and eastern North America suggest that these two regions were once part of one continuous plant and animal distribution.

Figure 3. *Pogonia ophioglossoides* as found in North America (left) and *Pogonia japonica* as found in eastern Asia (right).

Figure 4. *Pogonia ophioglossoides* (left) and *Pogonia japonica* (right) grown side by side.

Figure 5. *Nelumbo lutea* as found in North America (top) and *Nelumbo nucifera* as found in eastern Asia (bottom). Their hybrid form is fertile, indicating that they are really the same species.

EVOLUTION AND 'DEEP TIME'

The remarkable similarities between the plants and fungi of these two regions present a serious problem for evolutionists and their belief in 'deep time'. This is because, over millions of years, sister species, living on different continents and separated by huge distances over land/ocean, would be expected to evolve different characteristics. According to the theory of evolution, the ancestors of humans separated from other ape-like creatures around six million years ago. Between then and now, the evolutionary process allegedly gave rise to all the many changes that turned these creatures into the people we are today. It is difficult for evolutionists to explain why, over the same time period, the plants and fungi of eastern Asia and eastern North America did not evolve and change too!

Figure 7. The blue milk mushroom *Lactarius indigo* is found in Japan and eastern North America.

The similarities between the wildlife of these two regions, however, present no problem for biblical creationists. This is because, according to the Bible, none of the habitats found on the earth today can be older than around 4,500 years, the time of the global Flood, recorded in Genesis 6-8. It is possible that a continuous plant and animal distribution ensued linking eastern Asia and eastern North America due to the warm climate that existed at high latitudes directly after the Flood (fig. 2). This region may then have been split into two by the ensuing Ice Age and also the rising sea levels following its waning, around 800 years after the Flood.[8] ∎

Figure 6. The same species of mushroom *Tylopilus alboater* grows wild in both China and North America east of the Rocky Mountains.

References and notes

1. Wen, J., Evolution of the eastern Asian and eastern North American disjunct distributions in flowering plants, *Annual Review of Ecology and Systematics*, **30**:421–455, 1999.
2. Quian, H., Foristic relationships between eastern Asia and North America: test of Gray's hypothesis, *American Naturalist*, **160**(3):317–332, 2002.
3. Xiang, Q. *et al.*, Timing the Eastern Asian–Eastern North American Floristic Disjunction: Molecular Clock Corroborates Paleontological Estimates, *Molecular Phylogenetics and Evolution* **15**(3):462–472, 2000; cals.ncsu.edu/plantbiology/Faculty/xiang/Xianglab/www/Papers/XiangSoltis2000.pdf.
4. Ref. 2, p. 318.
5. Hongo, T. And Yokoyama, K., Mycofloristic ties of Japan to the continents, *Memoirs of the Faculty of Education of Shiga University* **28**:75–80, 1978; libdspace.biwako.shiga-u.ac.jp/dspace/bitstream/10441/3581/2/SJ07_0028_076A.pdf.
6. botit.botany.wisc.edu/courses/systematics/family_index/Family_Pages/Family_N_O/Nelumbonaceae.html.
7. Xue, J., *et al.*, Polymorphic chloroplast microsatellite loci in *Nelumbo* (Nelumbonaceae), *American Journal of Botany* e240–e244, 2012.
8. See Batten, D., ed., *The Creation Answers Book*, Creation Book Publishers, Queensland, Australia, ch. 16, 2009; creation.com/ice.

Article from *Creation* **35**(4):40–41 October 2013

DNA

MARVELLOUS MESSAGES OR MOSTLY MESS?

Jonathan Sarfati

ONE OF the most important discoveries of last century was the double helix structure of DNA. Its discoverers, James Watson, Francis Crick, and Maurice Wilkins, won the Nobel Prize for Physiology and Medicine in 1962 for their 1953 discovery.

The amazing design and complexity of living things provides strong evidence for a Creator. We know from the Bible that God rested from (i.e. finished) His creative work after Day 6 (Genesis 2:2–3) and now *sustains* His creation (Colossians 1:16–17, Hebrews 1:3). So how do complex living creatures arise *today*?

God's information technology

One aspect of this sustenance is that God has programmed the 'recipe' for all these structures on the famous double-helix molecule DNA (deoxyribonucleic acid). This recipe has an enormous *information content*, which is transmitted one generation to the next, so that living things reproduce 'after their kinds' (Genesis 1, 10 times). Leading atheistic evolutionist Richard Dawkins admits:

> [T]here is enough information capacity in a single human cell to store the Encyclopaedia Britannica, all 30 volumes of it, three or four times over.[1]

Just as the *Britannica* had intelligent writers to produce its information, so it is reasonable and even scientific to believe that the information in the living world likewise had an original compositor/sender. There is no known non-intelligent cause that has ever been *observed* to generate even a small portion of the literally encyclopedic information required for life.

The genetic code is not an outcome of raw chemistry, but of elaborate decoding machinery in the *ribosome*. Remarkably, this decoding machinery is itself encoded in the DNA, and the noted philosopher of science Sir Karl Popper pointed out:

> Thus the code can not be translated except by using certain products of its translation. This constitutes a baffling circle; a really vicious circle, it seems, for any attempt to form a model or theory of the genesis of the genetic code.[2]

So, such a system must be fully in place before it could work at all, a property called *irreducible complexity*. This means that it is impossible to be built by natural selection working on small changes.

DNA is by far the most compact information storage system in the universe. Even the simplest known living organism has 482 protein-coding genes. This is a total of 580,000 of four types of 'letters'[3]—humans have three billion in every nucleus. This is an incredibly high information density, about 1,000 terabytes per cubic millimetre (Tb/mm^3), way beyond current human technology.[4]

The 'letters' of DNA have another vital property due to their structure, which allows information to be transmitted: A pairs only with T, and C only with G, due to the chemical structures of the bases—the pair is like a rung or step on a spiral staircase. This means that the two strands of the double helix can be separated, and new strands can be formed that copy the information exactly. The new strand carries the same information as the old one, but instead of being like a photocopy, it is in a sense like a photographic negative. The copying is far more precise than pure chemistry could manage—only about 1 mistake in 10 billion copyings, because there is editing (proof-reading and error-checking) machinery, again encoded in the DNA. But how would the information for editing machinery be transmitted accurately before the machinery was in place? Lest it be argued that the accuracy could be achieved stepwise through selection, note that a high degree of accuracy is needed to prevent 'error catastrophe'—the accumulation of 'noise' in the form of junk proteins. Again there is a vicious circle (more irreducible complexity).

'on or off' patterns in a ferrimagnetic disk, and again the information is in the patterns, the arrangement, not the magnetic substance. Totally different media can carry exactly the same information. An example is this article you're reading—the information is exactly the same as that on my computer's hard disk drive (HDD), or more recently, my solid state drive, (SSD), but my page, HDD, and SSD look nothing like each other.

In DNA, the information is stored as sequences of four types of DNA bases, A, C, G and T (adenine, cytosine, guanine and thymine). In one sense, these could be called chemical 'letters' because they store information an analogous way to printed letters. There are huge problems

reader is familiar with the language. For example, a reader must know that the letter sequence c-a-t codes for a furry pet with retractable claws. But consider the sequence g-i-f-t—in English, it means a present; but in German, it means poison. After one creation talk in New Zealand where I pointed this out, a native German told me that when he was new to the country, he was appalled by its Christmas customs—trying to poison their families!

The unity of life

Many evolutionists claim that the DNA code is universal, and that this is proof of a common ancestor. But this is false—there are exceptions, some known since the 1970s. An example is *Paramecium*, where a few of the 64 (4^3 or $4{\times}4{\times}4$) possible codons code for different amino acids. More examples are being found constantly.[6] Also, some organisms code for one or two extra amino acids beyond the main 20 types.[7] But if one organism evolved into another with a different code, all the messages already encoded would be scrambled, just as written messages would be jumbled if typewriter keys were switched. This is a huge problem for the evolution of one code into another.

Also, in our cells we have 'power plants' called mitochondria, with their own genes. It turns out that they have a slightly different genetic code, too.

Certainly most of the code is universal, but this is best explained by common design—one Creator. Of all the millions of genetic codes possible, ours, or something almost like it, is optimal for protecting against errors.[8] But the created exceptions thwart attempts to explain the organisms by common-ancestry evolution.

The programs of life

Information is a measure of the complexity of the arrangement of parts of a storage medium, and doesn't depend on what parts are arranged. For instance, the printed page stores information via the 26 letters of the alphabet, which are arrangements of ink molecules on paper. But the information is not contained in the letters themselves. Even a translation into another language, even those with a different alphabet, need not change the information, but simply the way it is presented. However, a computer hard drive stores information in a totally different way—an array of magnetic

for evolutionists explaining how the 'letters' alone could come from a primordial soup. But even if this was solved, it would be as meaningless as getting a bowl of alphabet soup.[5]

The 'letters' must then link together in the face of chemistry trying to break them apart. Most importantly, the letters must be arranged correctly to have any meaning for life.

A group (codon) of three DNA 'letters' codes for one protein 'letter' called an amino acid, and the conversion is called translation. Since even one mistake in a protein can be catastrophic, it's important to decode correctly. Think again about a written language—it is only useful if the

Summary

- All living things have encyclopedic information content, a recipe for all their complex machinery and structures.
- This is stored and transmitted to the next generation as a message on DNA 'letters,' but the message is in the arrangement, not the letters themselves.
- The message requires decoding and transmission machinery, which itself is part of the stored 'message'.

- The choices of the code and even the letters are optimal.
- Therefore, the genetic coding system is an example of irreducible complexity.

Update: 'Junk DNA' concept junked

Many new wonders have been found in the amazing programming system of life since this article was published. A few are indicated in footnotes dated after 2003. But one of the most important is clearly refuting the concept of junk DNA.

Dawkins and others have claimed that this non-coding DNA is 'junk' or 'selfish' DNA. Supposedly, no intelligent designer would use such an inefficient system, therefore it must have evolved, they argue.

This parallels the 19th century claim that about a hundred 'vestigial organs' exist in the human body, i.e. allegedly useless remnants of our evolutionary history. But more enlightened evolutionists point out that the argument is logically invalid, because it is impossible *in principle* to prove that an organ has *no* function; rather, it could have a function we don't know about. One evolutionist also reminds us that "as our knowledge has increased the list of vestigial structures has decreased."[9]

So creationists for many years suspected that 'junk DNA' would be functional. And sure enough, since 2007, the ENCODE (Encyclopedia of DNA Elements) project has published dozens of papers that show that at least 80% of the so-called junk is transcribed into RNA, i.e. is *doing something*.[10] This includes micro RNAs (miRNA), very small molecules (about 22 nucleotides) that form a miRNA regulatory network or a genetic 'control panel'. This network includes *millions* of switches that turn protein-producing genes on or off,[11] controls gene splicing, and even governs the 3-D shape of the DNA in the nucleus and how this changes in time.[12] ■

References and notes

1. Dawkins, R., *The Blind Watchmaker*, W.W. Norton, New York, p. 115, 1986.
2. Popper, K.R., Scientific Reduction and the Essential Incompleteness of All Science; in Ayala, F. and Dobzhansky, T., Eds., *Studies in the Philosophy of Biology*, University of California Press, Berkeley, p. 270, 1974.
3. Fraser, C.M. *et al.*, The minimal gene complement of Mycoplasma genitalium, *Science* 270(5235):397–403, 1995; perspective by Goffeau, A., Life with 482 Genes, same issue, pp. 445–446.
4. Borthine, D., DNA storage could preserve data for millions of years, gizmag.com, 18 February 2015.
5. See Batten, D., Origin of life: An explanation of what is needed for abiogenesis (or biopoiesis), creation.com/origin-of-life, 26 November 2013
6. The genetic codes, *National Institutes of Health*, ncbi.nlm.nih.gov, last updated 18 November 2016.
7. Certain Archaea and eubacteria code for 21st or 22nd amino acids, selenocysteine and pyrrolysine—see Atkins, J.F. and Gesteland, R., The 22nd amino acid, *Science* 296(5572):1409–10, 24 May 2002.
8. Knight, J., Top translator, *New Scientist* 158(2130):15, 18 April 1998.
9. Scadding, S.R., Do 'vestigial organs' provide evidence for evolution? *Evolutionary Theory* 5(3):173–176, 1981.
10. See overview papers in *Nature* 489, 6 September 2012.
11. Batten, D., Dazzling DNA: Huge study highlights stupendous design in human DNA, *Creation* 35(1):38, 2013; creation.com/dazzling-dna.
12. Carter, R.W., The four dimensional human genome defies naturalistic explanations, creation.com/four-dimensional-genome, 6 October 2016.

INTRONS AND SPLICING

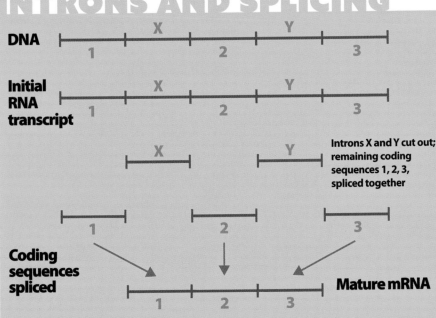

DNA X Y 1 2 3

Initial RNA transcript X Y 1 2 3

X Y Introns X and Y cut out; remaining coding sequences 1, 2, 3, spliced together

1 2 3

Coding sequences spliced 1 2 3 **Mature mRNA**

DNA is not read directly, but first the cell makes a negative copy in a very similar molecule called RNA (ribonucleic acid), a process called *transcription*, with a molecular machine called RNO polymerase (RNAP).[1] But in all organisms other than most bacteria, there is more to transcription. This RNA, reflecting the DNA, contains regions called exons that code for proteins, and non-coding regions called *introns*. So, the introns are removed and the exons are 'spliced' together to form the mRNA (messenger RNA) that is finally decoded to form the protein.

This also requires elaborate machinery called a *spliceosome*. This is assembled on the intron, chops it out at the right place and joins the exons together. This must be in the right direction and place, because, as shown above, it makes a huge difference if the exon is joined even one letter off. Thus, partly formed splicing machinery would be *harmful*, so natural selection would work *against* it.

And there is even a splicing code, which enables a single gene to encode multiple proteins. This explains why humans have only about 21,000 genes yet make up to a million proteins, which surprised those who decoded the human genome.[2]

References and notes

1. Sarfati, J., More marvellous machinery: 'DNA scrunching', *J. Creation* 21(1):4–5, 2007; creation.com/scrunching.
2. Carter, R.W., Splicing and dicing the human genome: Scientists begin to unravel the splicing code, creation.com/splicing, 1 July 2010.

Article from
Creation 25(2):26–31
March 2003

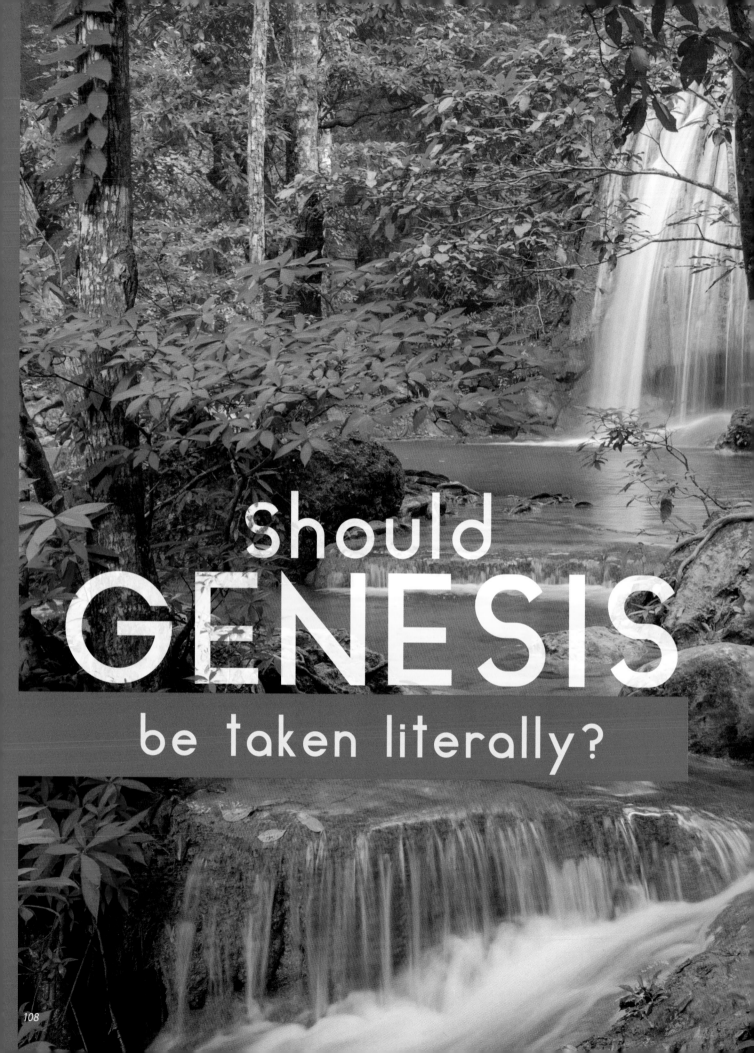

Should GENESIS be taken literally?

Weerayut Ranmai

■ **Russell Grigg**

CREATIONISTS ARE often accused of believing that the whole Bible should be taken literally. This is not so! Rather, the key to a correct understanding of any part of the Bible is to ascertain the *original meaning* of the portion or book under discussion. This is not as difficult as it may seem, as the Bible obviously contains:

- *Poetry*—as in the Psalms, where the repetition or parallelism of ideas is in accordance with Hebrew ideas of poetry, without the rhyme (parallelism of sound) and metre (parallelism of time) that are important parts of traditional English poetry. This, by the way, is the reason why the Psalms can be translated into other languages and still retain most of their literary appeal and poetic piquancy, while the elements of rhyme and metre are usually lost when traditional Western poetry is translated into other languages.
- *Parables*—as in many of the sayings of Jesus, such as the parable of the sower (Matthew 13:3–23), which Jesus Himself clearly states to be a parable and about which He gives meanings for the various items, such as the seed and the soil.
- *Prophecy*—as in the books of the last section of the Old Testament (Isaiah to Malachi).
- *Letters*—as in the New Testament epistles written by Paul, Peter, John, and others.
- *Biography*—as in the Gospels.
- *Autobiography/testimony*—as in the book of Acts where the author, Luke, after narrating the Apostle Paul's conversion on the road to Damascus as a historical fact (Acts 9:1–19), then describes two further occasions when Paul included this conversion experience as part of his own personal testimony (Acts 22:1–21; 26:1–22).
- *Authentic historical facts*—as in the books of 1 and 2 Kings, etc.

So the original meaning of any book of the Bible is usually quite clear from the author's style and the content. Who then was the author of Genesis, and how would his original readers have understood it given his style and the content of what he wrote?

The author

The Lord Jesus Himself and the Gospel writers said that the Law was given by Moses (Mark 10:3; Luke 24:27; John 1:17, 5:46–47), and the uniform tradition of the Jewish scribes and early Christian fathers, and the conclusion of conservative scholars to the present day, is that Genesis was written by Moses. This does not preclude the possibility that Moses had access to patriarchal records, preserved by being written on clay tablets and handed down from father to son via the line of Adam–Seth–Noah–Shem–Abraham–Isaac–Jacob, etc., as there are 11 verses in Genesis which read, "These are the generations [Hebrew: *toledoth* = 'origins' or by extension 'record of the origins'] of … ." (See Genesis 2:4; 5:1; 6:9; 10:1; 11:10; 11:27; 25:12; 25:19; 36:1; 36:9; 37:2.)

Chapters 12–50 of Genesis were very clearly written as authentic history, as they describe the lives of Abraham, Isaac, Jacob, and his 12 sons who were the ancestral heads of the 12 tribes of Israel. The Jewish people, from earliest biblical times to the present day, have always regarded this portion of Genesis as the true record of their nation's history.

So what about the first 11 chapters of Genesis, which are our main concern, as these are the ones that have incurred the most criticism from modern scholars, scientists, and skeptics?

Genesis 1–11
Are any of these chapters *poetry*?

To answer this question we need to examine in a little more depth just what is involved in the parallelism of ideas that constitutes Hebrew poetry.

Let us consider Psalm 1:1, which reads as follows: "Blessed is the man that walks not in the counsel of the wicked, nor stands in the way of sinners, nor sits in the seat of scoffers." Here we see triple parallelism in the nouns and verbs used

walks	counsel	wicked
stands	way	sinners
sits	seat	scoffers

(reading downwards in the following scheme):

As well as this overt parallelism, there is also a covert or subtle progression of meaning. In the first column, 'walks' suggests short-term

acquaintance, 'stands' implies readiness to discuss, and 'sits' speaks of long-term involvement. In the second column, 'counsel' betokens general advice, 'way' indicates a chosen course of action, and 'seat' signifies a set condition of mind. In the third column, 'wicked' describes the ungodly, 'sinner' characterizes the actively wicked, and 'scoffers' portrays the contemptuously wicked.

Other types of Hebrew poetry include contrastive parallelism, as in Proverbs 27:6, "Faithful are the wounds of a friend; profuse are the kisses of an enemy," and completive parallelism, as in Psalm 46:1, "God is our refuge and strength, a very present help in trouble."[1]

And so we return to our question. Are any of the first 11 chapters of Genesis poetry?

Answer: No, because these chapters do not contain information or invocation in any of the forms of Hebrew poetry, in either overt or covert form, and because Hebrew scholars of substance are agreed that this is so (see below).

Note: There certainly is repetition in Genesis chapter 1, e.g. "And God said …" occurs 10 times; "and God saw that it was good/very good" seven times; "according to their kinds" 10 times; "And there was evening and there was morning, [numbered] day" six times. However, these repetitions have none of the poetic forms discussed above; rather they are statements of fact and thus a record of what happened, and possibly for emphasis—to indicate the importance of the words repeated.

Internal evidence of the book of Genesis

There is the internal evidence of the book of Genesis itself. As already mentioned, chapters 12–50 have always been regarded by the Jewish people as being the record of their own true history, and the style of writing contained in chapters 1–11 is not strikingly different from that in chapters 12–50.

Hebrew scholars of standing have always regarded this to be the case. Thus, Professor James Barr, Regius Professor of Hebrew at the University of Oxford, has written:

Probably, so far as I know, there is no professor of Hebrew or Old Testament at any world-class university who does not believe that the writer(s) of Genesis 1–11 intended to convey to their readers the ideas that: (a) creation took place in a series of six days which were the same as the days of 24 hours we now experience (b) the figures contained in the Genesis genealogies provided by simple addition a chronology from the beginning of the world up to later stages in the biblical story (c) Noah's flood was understood to be world-wide and extinguish all human and animal life except for those in the ark. Or, to put it negatively, the apologetic arguments which suppose the 'days' of creation to be long eras of time, the figures of years not to be chronological, and the flood to be a merely local Mesopotamian flood, are not taken seriously by any such professors, as far as I know.[2]

One of the main themes of Genesis is the Sovereignty of God. This is seen in God's actions in respect of four outstanding events in Genesis 1–11 (Creation, the Fall, the Flood, and the Babel dispersion), and His relationship to four outstanding people in Genesis 12–50 (Abraham, Isaac, Jacob, and Joseph). There is thus a unifying theme to the whole of the book of Genesis, which falls to the ground if any part is mythical and not true history; on the other hand, each portion reinforces the historical authenticity of the other.[3]

Evidence from the rest of the Bible

- The principal people mentioned in Genesis chapters 1–11 are referred to as real—historical, not mythical—people in the rest of the Bible, often many times. For example, *Adam, Eve, Cain, Abel,* and *Noah* are referred to in 15 other books of the Bible.
- The Lord Jesus Christ referred to the Creation of Adam and Eve as a real historical event, by quoting Genesis 1:27 and 2:24 in His teaching about divorce (Matthew 19:3–6; Mark 10:2–9). He also referred to Noah as a real historical person and the Flood as a real historical event, in His teaching about the "coming of the Son of Man" (Matthew 24:37–39;

A Babylonian tablet fragment found at Nippur, an ancient Babylonian site in the same general location that Abraham came from. The area outlined in black is a record about the Flood. There are more than 300 known records of the Flood world-wide, with about 30 of them in writing. Some are remarkably close in their details to the original—the biblical account.

Photo Dr Clifford Wilson (1923–2012)

Luke 17:26–27), the divine figure foretold in Daniel 7 (see also "Is Jesus Christ the Creator God?", p. 34).

- Unless the first 11 chapters of Genesis are authentic historical events, the rest of the Bible is incomplete and incomprehensible as to its full meaning. The theme of the Bible is Redemption, and may be outlined thus:

1. God's redeeming purpose is revealed in Genesis 1–11,
2. God's redeeming purpose progresses from Genesis 12 to Jude 25, and
3. God's redeeming purpose is consummated in Revelation 1–22.

But why does mankind need to be redeemed? What is it that he needs to be redeemed from? The answer is given in Genesis 1–11, namely, from the ruin brought about by sin. Unless we know that the entrance of sin to the human race was a true historical fact, God's purpose in providing a substitutionary atonement is a mystery. Conversely, the historical truth of Genesis 1–11 shows that all mankind has come under the righteous anger of God and needs salvation from the penalty, power, and presence of sin.

- Unless the events of the first chapters of Genesis are true history, the Apostle Paul's explanation of the Gospel in Romans

chapter 5 and of the resurrection in 1 Corinthians chapter 15 has no meaning. Paul writes:

For as by the one man's [Adam's] disobedience the many were made sinners, so by the one man's [Christ's] obedience the many will be made righteous. (Romans 5:19). For as by a man came death, by a man has come also the resurrection of the dead. For as in Adam all die, so also in Christ shall all be made alive. … Thus it is written, 'The first man Adam became a living being'; the last Adam became a life-giving spirit. (1 Corinthians 15:21–22; 45).

The historical truth of the record concerning the first Adam is a guarantee that what God says in His Word about the last Adam [Jesus] is also true. Likewise, the historical, literal truth of the record concerning Jesus is a guarantee that what God says about the first Adam is also historically and literally true.

Conclusion

We return to the question which forms the title of this article. Should Genesis be taken literally?

Answer: If we apply the normal principles of biblical exegesis (ignoring pressure to make the text conform to the evolutionary prejudices of our age), it is overwhelmingly obvious that Genesis was meant to be taken in a straightforward, obvious sense as an authentic, literal, historical record of what actually happened. ∎

References and notes

1. This discussion of Hebrew poetry was adapted from Baxter, J.S., *Explore the Book,* Vol. 1, pp. 13–16, Zondervan, 1966.
2. Letter from Professor James Barr to David C.C. Watson of the UK, dated 23 April 1984. Copy held by the author. Note that Prof. Barr does not claim to believe that Genesis is historically true; he is just telling us what, in his opinion, the language was meant to convey.
3. Adapted from J. Sidlow Baxter, *Explore the Book,* Vol. 1, pp. 27–29.

Article from
Creation **16**(1):38-41
December 1993

POLYSTRATE FOSSILS
EVIDENCE FOR A YOUNG EARTH

■ **Tas Walker**

TREE TRUNK fossils are frequently found cutting across many geological layers—hence the name polystrate fossils (poly = many; stratum = layer).

It is not possible that polystrate fossils were buried gradually over many thousands or hundreds of thousands of years because the top part of any tree would have rotted away before it could be protected by sediment. Polystrate fossils point to rapid burial and are evidence for the reality of the global Flood recorded in the Bible.

This is how Derek Ager, Emeritus Professor of Geology, University College of Swansea, trained under strict Lyellian uniformitarianism, [1] describes some polystrate fossil tree trunks that he illustrated in his book:

"If one estimates the total thickness of the British Coal Measures as about

Article from
Creation **29**(3):54–55
June 2007

Eroding cliffs (above) at Joggins, Nova Scotia, reveal abundant polystrate tree trunks (left and below) and horizontal coalified wood (right).

Photos by Ian Juby

1000 m, laid down in about 10 million years, then, assuming a constant rate of sedimentation, it would have taken 100 000 years to bury a tree 10 m high, which is ridiculous.

"Alternatively, if a 10 m tree were buried in 10 years, that would mean 1000 km in a million years or 10 000 km in 10 million years (i.e. the duration of the coal measures). This is equally ridiculous and we cannot escape the conclusion that *sedimentation was at times very rapid indeed* and at other times there were long breaks in sedimentation, *though it looks both uniform and continuous*"[2] [*emphasis* added].

Derek Ager was no Bible believer, in fact he was disparaging of creationists, yet he could see, in spite of his training, that the geological evidence pointed to rapid sedimentation and burial.

Further, although sedimentation looked "uniform and continuous", he assumed that there had to be 'long breaks in sedimentation". Why? To preserve the idea that the earth is millions of years old—in spite of the evidence.

Polystrate fossils provide direct evidence that the rocks formed rapidly, consistent with a young creation, as the Bible reports.[3] ■

References and notes

1. Charles Lyell argued that all geology could be explained by slow, uniform processes over eons of time. Catastrophes were not allowed.
2. Ager, D.V., *The New Catastrophism*, Cambridge University Press, p. 49, 1993; emphasis added.
3. Ref. 2, fig 4.5, p. 48.

Above: Ager's illustration—an old print showing fossil trees that appear to be in growth position at Nant Llech in the Swansea Valley, South Wales, UK. The trees are now preserved outside Swansea Museum.[3]

Russell Grigg

'THE MIND of God' is a term that Christians use to mean 'the reason(s) why God does something'. It is also the title of a book by Dr Paul Davies, Professor of Mathematical Physics at the University of Adelaide in South Australia.[1] It is also the concluding phrase in physicist Stephen Hawking's best-selling book *A Brief History of Time*, in which he says, "If we find the answer to that [i.e. why it is that we and the universe exist], it would be the ultimate triumph of human reason—for then we would know the mind of God."[2]

The 'evolution' of the 'big bang'

In the twentieth century, the first version of the 'big bang' as the explosion of a 'primeval atom' was put forward by Abbé Georges-Henri Lemaître in 1931. Lemaître already knew of Edwin Hubble's work on the redshift of light from distant stars (which Hubble interpreted to mean that the universe is expanding), and by extrapolating backwards in time, he postulated that the universe originated as a single particle of vast energy but near-zero radius.[3] He argued (erroneously) that cosmic rays must have come from such an explosion.

In 1965, a version of the 'big bang' was put forward by Robert Dicke, P.J.E. Peebles and others, which appeared to receive some confirmation by the accidental discovery by Arno Penzias and Robert Wilson that the universe seemed to be uniformly filled with very even heat at a temperature of about 3 K.[4] (K is the symbol for kelvin, the base unit of thermodynamic temperature.) This was interpreted as being the after-glow in the form of microwave radiation left over from a huge initial explosion, hugely 'red-shifted'. It became inconceivable that the 'big bang' theory could be wrong, and entire careers in cosmology have been built on the presumption that the 'big bang' was fact.

However, calculations have shown that the detected matter in the universe is only about 1% of the amount required to produce the gravitational attraction needed to form all the galaxies and clumps of galaxies, even within the vast time span of a hypothetical 15 billion years.

This problem was solved with a stroke of the pen. In the early 1980s, cosmological theoreticians decided that nearly 99% of the universe was now made up of 'cold dark matter' (CDM)—necessarily 'dark' because no one has ever seen it or detected it, and up to 99 times the amount of the visible matter in the universe.[5]

Cosmic Microwave Background (CMB)

Another problem was the very smoothness of the so-called background radiation. But the randomness produced by a 'big bang' would have had very different temperatures in different regions of space. So how did it become so uniform? Only by exchanging radiation, i.e. light. The CMB is supposed to have been emitted when space first became transparent, 300,000 years after the big bang. But the universe's background temperature was already uniform over a range 10 times greater than light could have travelled (300,000 light years).

So how did the universe become so uniform past the distance light could have travelled, i.e., its 'horizon'? This 'horizon

The mind of GOD and the 'big bang'

problem' is a vexing problem for big bang theory. The main solution is space itself expanding much faster than light for a short time, with no known mechanism to start or stop this, while gravity was reversed.[6] Because this is so ad hoc, other big bangers have proposed that light itself was much faster.[7]

And more than two decades ago, two Soviet scientists, Sunyaev and Zel'dovich, pointed out that as the background radiation passes through large clouds of intergalactic gas, the resultant change in intensity could cause these 'lumps'. But where are the shadows in the CMB?[8,9]

What happened before the 'big bang'?

Paul Davies's reply is, "According to modern physics, the big bang represented the origin of space and time, as well as of matter and energy. This means that *time itself came into existence with the big bang.* Questions like: What happened before the big bang? or What caused the big bang? are therefore meaningless. There was no before."[10] And Stephen Hawking claims that under certain conditions the universe "would have neither beginning nor end: it would simply be. What place, then, for a creator?"[11]

How did nothing become something and then explode?

Paul Davies's answer is that it happened through quantum physics applied to cosmology. He says, "This 'quantum cosmology' provides a loophole for the universe to, so to speak, spring into existence from nothing, without violating any laws of physics."[12] This is very significant, as it shows the fallibility of theistic evolution. Theistic evolutionists often urge what is in effect retreat to a 'God of the gaps' idea. God is invoked as necessary to create the initial particle and to 'light the fuse' as it were—thereafter the rest can evolve more or less by itself. However, Hawking says his new theory has no moment of creation and requires no creator. Where does this leave theistic evolutionary compromise?

What should we believe?

What should Bible-believing Christians think about all this and believe? There are certain contra facts which are indisputable and certain principles that Christians should always use in evaluating naturalistic theories about origins.

1.   Not all secular cosmogonists agree with the concept of the 'big bang'; in fact, many have never supported it.[13,14]

2.   The 'big bang' scenario involves tremendous (even infinite) energy at the beginning, but supplies no explanation for the source of this energy. Nor is it clear how the gravity of the initial universal black hole can be overcome by a 'quantum fluctuation'. Jargon like this seems to be part of an expanding vocabulary of 'big-bang-speak', masking some formidable, if not insuperable, difficulties. There is also no convincing explanation as to why an outward spray of gas radiating from the 'big bang' should form galaxies, stars, and planets.

3.   The big bang is based on the assumption that the universe has no centre. For nearly 20 years astronomer William G. Tifft of the University of Arizona has been claiming that his accurate measurements of galaxy redshifts show that redshifts are 'quantized', or 'tend to fall on evenly spaced values, like rungs of a

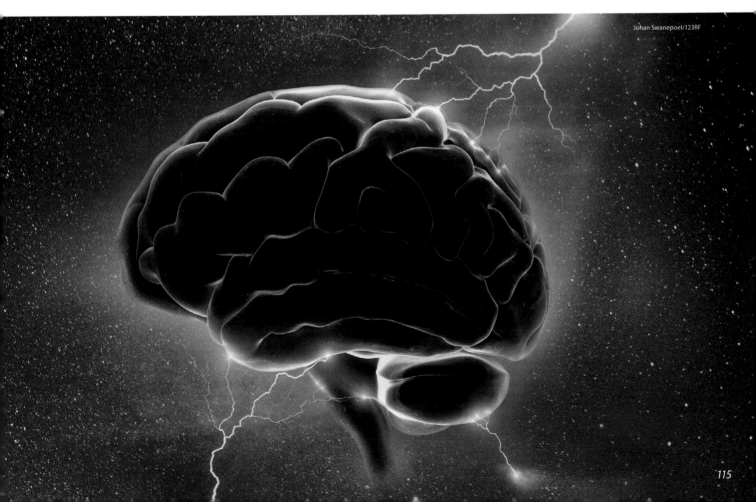

Johan Swanepoel/123RF

ladder', not in a smooth manner as would be expected if the universe was centerless. So some astronomers are beginning to wonder what the redshifts really mean.[15,16]

4.   To believe that the known universe was once condensed into a point of zero dimensions takes an unimaginable leap of faith; in fact, much more faith than it takes to believe that God created everything in the way He says He did in Genesis. The 'big bang' is a major part of the 'creation myth' of the Western nations' major religion—secular humanism.

5.   With the passage of time, the lack of proven evidence for the 'big bang' has led some scientists to make such remarks as, "Never has such a mighty edifice been built on such insubstantial foundations."[17] And, "You have to understand that first there is speculation, then there is wild speculation, and then there is cosmology."[18]

6.   Did God create by means of the 'big bang' or provide the initial energy to kick off the 'big bang'? No! It contradicts the biblical cosmogony. The order of events is different—for example, this theory claims that the sun existed long before the earth, whereas Genesis says the earth was created before the sun. Furthermore, the time-frame is quite different (refer Exodus 20:11). Also, we have seen that Hawking, Davies *et al.* would repudiate any such threat to the self-creating power of their evolutionary universe.[19] It is sad indeed that theistic evolutionists (including some who would deny such a title) are urging Christians to say 'Yes'.

7.   In taking the above attitude, are Christians in danger of repeating the error of the seventeenth-century Church when it opposed Galileo for suggesting a heliocentric (sun-centred) mechanism for our planetary system? Answer: tying the Bible with the big bang would be the same mistake as Galileo's opponents in the scientific establishment and the church: trying to tie the Bible with the 'science' of its day: Aristotelian/Ptolemaic absolute-geocentrist cosmology.[20]

By contrast, the 'big bang' and all other theories of origins that are based on human philosophies attempt to say how the universe made itself by its own processes and properties, and with no supernatural input.

Conclusions

Christians do not need Hawking's elusive 'grand unified theory' of the universe to know the mind of God or to know who they are, why they exist, and where they are going. We already have access to the mind of God in the Bible. This tells us that through repentance and faith in the atoning work of Christ on the cross we become children of God, that we are here to worship and serve the living God, and that one day we who love God and have received His Son the Lord Jesus Christ will go to live with Him for ever. In fact, the 'grand unified theory' and the 'theory of everything' is the Bible!

As matters stand at present, there is no better astronomic theory for the origin of the universe than the inspired explanation of the Bible, "By the word of the LORD the heavens were made, and by the breath of his mouth all their host. … For he spoke, and it came to be; he commanded, and it stood firm" (Psalm 33:6, 9). ■

References and notes

1   Davies, P., *The Mind of God*, Penguin Books, London, 1992. Compare Batten, D., Physicists' God-talk, *Creation* **17**(3):15, 1995.

2   Hawking, S.W., *A Brief History of Time*, Bantam Books, London, 1988.

3   Lemaître, G., *The Primeval Atom: An Essay on Cosmogony*, Van Nostrand, NY, 1950.

4   In due course refined to 2.736 Kelvin (i.e. 2.736 degrees above absolute zero), equivalent to -270.5°C.

5   Hartnett, J., Is 'dark matter' the unknown god? *Creation* **37**(2):22–24, 2015; creation.com/dark-matter-god.

6   Hartnett, J., Cosmic Inflation: Did it really happen? creation.com/inflation, 11 September 2015.

7   Hartnett, J., Does the new much-faster-speed-of-light theory fix the big bang's problems? creation.com/faster-light, 26 January 2017.

8   Sunyaev R. A. and Zeldovitch, Y.B., 'Small-scale fluctuations of relic radiation', *Astrophysics and Space Science* **7**(1):3–19, 1970.

9   Hartnett, J., 'Light from the big bang' casts no shadows, *Creation* **37**(1):50–51, 2015; creation.com/shadows.

10 Davies, P., 'Science, God and the Laws of the Universe', *ABC Radio 24 Hours*, August 1992, p. 36–39; emphasis in original.

11 Davies, Ref. 2, p. 149.

12 Hawking, Ref. 10, p. 37.

13 Lerner, E., Bucking the big bang, *New Scientist* **182**(2448):20, 22 May 2004.

14 Wieland, C., Secular scientists blast the big bang, What now for naïve apologetics? *Creation* **27**(2):23–25 2005; creation.com/big-bang-blast.

15 B.N.G. Guthrie and W.M. Napier, 'Evidence for red shift perodicity in nearby field galaxies', *Mon. Not. R. Astr. Soc.* **253**:533–544, 1991; and Gribbin, J., '"Bunched" red shifts question cosmology', *New Scientist* **1800**:21–28, December 1991.

16 Demick, D. and Wieland, C., In the middle of the action, *Creation* **28**(1):52–55, 2005; creation.com/quantized.

17 Editorial comment in *New Scientist* **1853**:3, December 1992, p. 3.

18 Harris, M, "Stephen Hawking: Genius or Pretender", in Focus on Science, *The Weekend Australian*, 4–5 July 1992, p. 19.

19 See Ref. 1., pp. 58–61, 68, 171.

20 Grigg, R., The Galileo 'twist', *Creation* **19**(4):30–32, 1997; creation.com/gal-twist.

Update: This classic article was republished on creation.com in 2010, i.e. after almost 17 years. Yet after all this time, it still is a fine overview of the big picture. The only updating needed here is mostly indicated by footnote references from papers written after 1993, to developments that reinforce the points made in the articles.

Andrey Kryuchkov/123RF

Article from
Creation **15**(4):38-43
September 1993

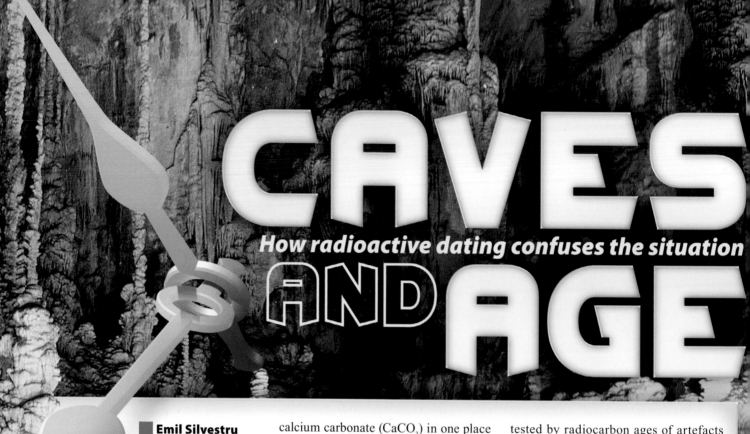

CAVES

How radioactive dating confuses the situation

AND AGE

Emil Silvestru

CAVES ARE a common feature of karst landscapes—the rugged sort formed in rocks that dissolve easily such as limestone (mainly calcium carbonate), forming underground passages and drainages. Caves have always been considered the perfect archive, preserving the past, unlike most other environments. And they offer evolutionary scientists an array of items aching to be radiometrically dated.

These include the inspiring stone decorations called speleothems—such as stalactites (on the ceiling), stalagmites (on the floor) and flowstone. These formed when water enriched by dissolved carbon dioxide (CO_2)—making it acidic— dissolved the alkaline calcium carbonate ($CaCO_3$) in one place and released the mineral in another.[1]

Evolutionists claim speleothems formed over hundreds of thousands of years. But in my own evolutionary days, I had never considered an important consequence of such an age: the tiny water droplet, which built that stalagmite, had to keep arriving at precisely the same spot on the floor of the cave for 100,000 years!

Well, I knew—and all karstologists know—that the surface of limestone terrains above caves changes dramatically in short periods of time. And any change at the surface also changes the location of the water droplets inside the cave. However, the stalagmites do not indicate any changes. So the conclusion is simple: they cannot be that old. And that fact indicates the old-age belief is fallacious.

Radiometric dating

Speleothems are amenable to the uranium-thorium ($^{234}U/^{230}Th$) method of dating, and caves are assumed to be much less prone to variations of all sorts. Sometimes the 'measured' ages of speleothems can be tested by radiocarbon ages of artefacts and fossils found in caves. Speleothems are believed to preserve accurate records of ancient climates—or paleoclimates. This is because they preserve oxygen and carbon isotope ratios from the past, and that allows scientists to make paleoclimate reconstructions.

Radiometric dating however often disagrees with the observed growth rates of speleothems and their complex formation processes,[2] and this confuses attempts to make sense of speleothem interpretations. As for paleoclimate reconstructions, one must understand well how any variation in climate could have affected the isotopic ratios and accurately relate these to the speleothem record.

Speleothems and ice cover

On the use of climate variations, karstological wisdom maintains that during the Ice Age the water infiltrating into caves either stopped or significantly diminished. At this time, ice covered much of the ground and even where it didn't, beyond the ice sheets, permafrost was extensive. With less water it is expected that the growth of speleothems would be arrested or much diminished. This is a soundly-based understanding of how past environments would affect speleothem development.

Yet, this karstological wisdom is contradicted by most of the speleothems studied from areas that are known to have been affected by the ice cover! The reason is all to do with the dates that have been assigned by radioactive dating.

Because of the 'dates', evolutionists concluded that speleothems grew fast when they should not have grown, and did not grow when they should have! Rather than discard the dates, most evolutionary scientists prefer to discard all 'unorthodox' speleothems, and use only the few that match their grand scheme of things.

Vancouver Island karst

Some of the contradictory results have come from the karst on Vancouver Island, Canada, which has provided only a few datable speleothems. The reason for the paucity of specimens is that the island was covered by up to 2 km (6,500 ft) of ice during the Fraser Glaciation, the most intense episode of glaciation during the Ice Age. Understandably, the speleothems did not grow when ice covered the landscape, and after the ice melted, the caves are too young to have a large number of speleothems. In fact all North American karst terrains that have been covered by ice have similar characteristics.

Also, massive amounts of meltwater, running beneath the ice sheet, repeatedly flooded Vancouver Island caves. This is revealed by the frequent and large rounded boulders inside many caves, some transported by moving water from a considerable distance. This would have destroyed any speleothems and prevented new ones from forming. Thus, in North America, only caves south of the ice cover during the Ice Age are rich in speleothems. The Vancouver Island speleothems have yielded radiometric ages of between 12 and 18 thousand years.[3,4]

That creates a problem and causes confusion. According to various geological evidences, the island was covered by ice, so the speleothems should not have grown at this time. But rather than question the radio-isotopic dates (and hence the methodology involved), some scientists have proposed that the 2-km– (6,500-ft–) thick ice cover melted and grew back in a few thousand years, even though there is no evidence for this melting and they cannot explain how it could have happened! Of course, a simpler explanation is that the radiometric dating is incorrect and that the speleothems grew only *after* the ice had melted.

Arch Cave

Another contradictory result was uncovered by scientists studying a speleothem from Arch Cave on Vancouver Island. They nonchalantly stated that the cave was "chosen for its proximity to the ocean so as to reflect a global climate history, and for its abundance of accessible cave deposits that were distant enough from the cave entrance and ground surface to mitigate any seasonal temperature effects." In other words, they envisaged that speleothem growth on the ancient shore lines on the east coast of Vancouver Island would allow meaningful global correlation as the world's sea level oscillated during the Ice Age—rising and falling as ice was locked on continents or melted.

Based on the measured oxygen and carbon isotopes (^{18}O and ^{13}C) they reconstructed the paleoclimate from the speleothem, which was radiometrically dated at 12,500 years. Yet, the geological evidence indicates the island was covered by ice at that time, so there should have been no speleothems growing at all. Not only the island, but the nearby Strait of Georgia was completely plugged by ice, with glacial scouring still visible on the bottom. In spite of this, maintaining their unshakable confidence in radiometric dating, the scientists conveniently ignored these geological facts and claimed the speleothems grew beneath the ice cover.

Article from
Creation **34**(1):46–48
January 2012

But if there really was this much ice cover at the time that the speleothems grew, the water infiltrating into the caves would not reflect the atmospheric composition at the time (as rainwater infiltrating into caves does today). Rather it would reflect an unreliable mixture of water from the melted ice layers. That would render any paleoclimate reconstruction from speleothems meaningless. Under such circumstances the 'global climate history' cannot be reconstructed and cannot be directly correlated with data from the caves.

In other words, by uncritically accepting the radioactive date without question, the researchers have ended up with a scheme that contradicts the geological evidence and undermines the basis for making paleoclimate reconstructions in the first place.

Clearing the confusion

On the other hand, when we apply some scientific skepticism to the spurious dates, we uncover a rather simple and consistent scenario that is in perfect accordance with the Genesis record. This allows us to understand the proper sequence of events, with the effects of Noah's Flood being the key. The caves on Vancouver Island formed after the Flood and during the Ice Age.[5] As creationist geologists have so simply documented, the Ice Age was a consequence of the warmer oceans and cooler land that existed on the earth immediately after the Flood (see "What caused the Ice Age?", p. 46). Only when the ice from the Ice Age had retreated did speleothems start growing inside those caves, and these have recorded the postglacial climate variations over the last 4,000 years. ■

References and notes

1. Lewis, D., Rapid stalactite growth in Siberia, *Creation* **32**(1):40–42, 2009; creation.com/stalactite.
2. Silvestru, E., Caves for all seasons, *Creation* **25**(3):44–49, 2003; creation.com/all-seasons.
3. Latham, A.G., Schwarcz, H.P. and Ford, D.C., Secular variation in the Earth's magnetic field from 18.5 to 15.0 ka BP, as recorded in a Vancouver Island stalagmite, *Canadian J. Earth Sciences* **24**:1235–1241, 1987.
4. Marshall, D., Bassam, G., Countess, R. and Gabities, J., Preliminary paleoclimate reconstruction based on a 12,500 year old speleothem from Vancouver Island, Canada: Stable isotopes and U–Th disequilibrium dating, *Quaternary Science Reviews* **XXX**:1–7, 2009.
5. Silvestru, E., *Geology and Cave Formation: A Post-Flood Story*, DVD, creation.com/s/30-9-528.

Emil Silvestru, Ph.D.
Dr Silvestru earned his geology Ph.D in karst sedimentology at Romania's Babes-Bolyai University (where he was once an associate professor). A world authority on the geology of caves, he has published 41 scientific papers, written one book, The Cave Book—available through creation.com—and co-authored two others. Fluent in five languages and a popular presenter, he was a fulltime speaker/scientist for CMI-Canada from 1997 until a debilitating stroke in 2012. For more: creation.com/emil-silvestru.

The world's second largest subterranean glacier in cave Ghețarul de la Scărișoara, 80 m (260 feet) below ground. Note the asymmetry of the copious ice stalagmites standing on the floor. These change shape every year. The curved sides stand towards the deeper, warmer parts of the cave, away from the colder zone around the ice block.

Article from
Creation **37**(2):47–49
April 2015

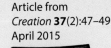

THE NAME
GAME

scientific ideas named after creationists

SHAUN DOYLE

CAN CREATIONISTS be real scientists? High priest of Darwinism Richard Dawkins doesn't seem to think so:

"It is absolutely safe to say that if you meet somebody who claims not to believe in evolution, that person is ignorant, stupid or insane (or wicked, but I'd rather not consider that)."[1]

And apparently we can trust Dawkins' assessment, since recently a genus of fish has been named after him—*Dawkinsia*.[2] In the words of lead researcher Rohan Pethiyagoda:

"Richard Dawkins has through his writings helped us understand that the universe is far more beautiful and awe-inspiring than any religion has imagined. We hope that *Dawkinsia* will serve as a reminder of the elegance and simplicity of evolution, the only rational explanation there is for the unimaginable diversity of life on Earth."[3]

One evolutionist blogger commenting on this gleefully proclaimed: "Your move, Creationists."[4]

We might call this the 'name game challenge'. Things in science are named after people who have made significant contributions to science all the time. No doubt Pethiyagoda thought he was doing that in naming the new fish genus *Dawkinsia*. But do creationists have anything in science named after them?

Science and its laws

A good place to start is a commonly practised scientific method—often called the Baconian method. It was named after English scientist and philosopher Francis Bacon (1561–1626). He was the first to systematically explain how we do science. He believed in biblical creation, and was an English Protestant.[5] He was even motivated by trying to regain the knowledge he believed that Adam had before the Fall.[6]

However, not only science itself, but many of its laws are named after Christians. For example, there are Kepler's three laws of planetary motion,

which describe the way planets move around the sun. They were named after devout Lutheran and biblical creationist Johannes Kepler (1571–1630) who discovered them. The German Kepler also gave us the famous phrase that science is "thinking God's thoughts after him."[7]

Englishman Isaac Newton (1642/3–1727) hardly needs introduction; he is generally regarded as the most influential scientist of all time. He explained the

cause of Kepler's laws in what are known as 'Newton's three laws of motion' and his theory of universal gravitation—the law of gravity. In these he showed that the heavens obey the same laws of motion as the earth. Newton also has the fundamental unit of force named after him—the newton (N). And like Kepler, Newton was a biblical creationist, who wrote far more on the Bible and theology than he ever did on science.[8]

Robert Boyle (1627–1691) is known as the father of modern chemistry. In his famous book, *The Skeptical Chymist,* the Anglo-Irishman Boyle overturned the then popular notion that everything is made up of four elements: fire, water, earth, and air. He redefined the 'element' to give us our modern notion of an element—a substance that cannot be separated into simpler components by chemical methods. He is also known for Boyle's Law, which states that a gas's volume increases as its pressure decreases at a constant temperature. He was a generous patron of missionary work, and wrote a number of books defending the Christian faith. He too was a biblical creationist.[9]

Another famous law of chemistry s Dalton's Law, which states that the total pressure exerted by the mixture of non-reactive gases is equal to the sum of the partial pressures of individual gases. It was named after John Dalton (1766–1844), a devout English Quaker who was well known for his simple and steadfast devotion to practical Christian piety.[10]

Perhaps the greatest achievement of 19th century physics was Maxwell's equations, a set of four fundamental equations that light and all forms of electromagnetic radiation obey. They were named after the brilliant Scotsman who brought together various streams of thought in such an elegant way, James Clerk Maxwell (1831–1879). Clerk Maxwell was also a devout evangelical and biblical creationist.[11,12]

Units of measurement

Another area of naming common in science, already introduced with Isaac Newton, is that of units of measurement. SI units are the internationally recognized standards of scientific measurement. Of this system, those known as SI base units, seven in all, are its fundamental units (see table 1). Of the seven, only two are

BASE QUANTITY	SI BASE UNIT	
length	metre	m
mass	kilogram	kg
time	second	s
electric current	ampere	A
thermodynamic temperature	kelvin	K
amount of substance	mole	mol
luminous intensity	candela	cd

Table 1. SI base units. Those highlighted are named after scientists.

named after people: the kelvin and the ampere. The *kelvin* is the SI base unit of temperature. It was named after the British Lord Kelvin (William Thomson, 1824–1907), one of the founders of the field of thermodynamics. He believed that the earth could have been up to 40 million years old based on his calculations, but he was a Christian and a creationist.[13] The *ampere* is the SI base unit of electric current. It was named after André-Marie Ampère (1775–1836), a French mathematician and physicist and devout Catholic creationist.[14]

However, many other SI units, known as *derived* units, are also named after creationists. The *newton* (N) is the SI derived unit for force. The *pascal* (Pa) is the SI unit for pressure, and was named after French scientist and Christian Blaise Pascal (1623–1662), who is also known for Pascal's wager and a number of classic theological and philosophical writings (such as *Pensées*).[15] The *joule* (J) is the SI unit for energy, and was named after the Englishman James Joule (1818–1889). Joule often collaborated with Lord Kelvin, and was a firm believer in the Bible.[16] The *farad* (F) is the SI unit for capacitance, which is named after Michael Faraday (1791–1867). Faraday is often recognized as the greatest experimentalist of all time, and though English, he was a member of a conservative offshoot of the Church of Scotland called the Sandemanians, very strict on standing on biblical authority.

Science: littered with the names of creationists

Here are some more beneficial ideas that have come about through scientific research by creationists:

- Pasteurization—the process where a food is heated to a given temperature for a set amount of time, and cooled very quickly, which kills off most pathogenic germs in food. It was named after its inventor, Roman Catholic creationist Louis Pasteur. Louis Pasteur (1822–1895) championed the French fight against Darwin's ideas by showing that since life only comes from life, Darwin's evolution could never get started.[17]

- The Mercator projection—a standard projection used in mapping which enables straight line drawings of voyages with a constant heading. It was developed by the Flemish Christian Gerardus Mercator (1512–1594).[18]
- The Faraday cage—an enclosure formed by any metal that conducts electricity which acts as a shield against electric currents and (to differing extents) electromagnetic radiation to anything inside. This was first discovered by the American Benjamin Franklin (1706–1790), but first explained by Michael Faraday.[19]

More examples could be added. So what scientific ideas have we seen are named after creationists? The foundational laws of motion, chemistry, and electromagnetism. The only two SI base units named after people, and numerous SI derived units. A number of widely used processes and inventions. And perhaps most significantly—the commonly practised scientific method itself. Unlike *Dawkinsia,* these things were not named after these people for some nebulous achievement unrelated to the actual discovery—these people *made* these discoveries. And they were all trying to do just as Kepler did—thinking God's thoughts after Him.

The history of science is one of the most compelling testimonies to the reality and practical power of the Bible. Not only can creationists be real scientists, real science only blossomed under creationist assumptions![20] Thinking God's thoughts after Him is just one practical outworking of Genesis 1:27–28—we were created in God's image to rule creation. To rule as God rules, we must understand. And to understand the creation and how it works, we must test it. ■

SHAUN DOYLE
obtained a Bachelor of Environmental Science (Hons.) and a Graduate Diploma in Natural Resource Studies from the University of Queensland, Brisbane, Australia. For more: creation.com/shaun-doyle.

References and notes

1. Cited in Dawkins, R., Ignorance is no crime, old. richarddawkins.net, 15 May 2006.
2. Catchpoole, D., Fishy *Dawkinsia* tales, tragic Dawkinsian philosophy, creation.com/fishy-dawkinsia, 28 August 2012.
3. Sri Lankans name new type of fish after Richard Dawkins, 16 July 2012, telegraph.co.uk, accessed 11 April 2013.
4. Mehta, H., New genus of South Asian fish named after Richard Dawkins, 16 July 2012, patheos.com/blogs/friendlyatheist, as at 12 April 2013.
5. Bacon's impact was not entirely positive. While he believed in biblical creation, he also advocated a separation between the Bible and science. They were in his mind *equally authoritative*, but they spoke to different aspects of reality. This led to the subsuming of the Bible under science, and the ultimate rejection of the Bible in favour of science. Bacon, F., *The Advancement of Learning*, 1.6.16,1605; gutenberg.org, acc. 9 April 2013.
6. Harrison, P., *The Fall of Man and the Foundations of Science*, Cambridge University Press, 2007. See also a review of this book, Weinberger, L., The Fall and the inspiration for science, *J. Creation* **4**(3):18–21, 2010; creation.com/fallscience.
7. Lamont, A., Johannes Kepler: Outstanding scientist and committed Christian, *Creation* **15**(1):40–43, December 1992; creation.com/kepler.
8. Lamont, A., Sir Isaac Newton (1642/3–1727): a scientific genius, *Creation* **12**(3):48–51, June 1990; creation.com/newton.
9. Doolan, R., The man who turned chemistry into a science: Robert Boyle (1627–1691), *Creation* **12**(1):22–23, December 1989; creation.com/boyle.
10. Graves, D., *Scientists of Faith*, Kregel, Grand Rapids, MI, pp. 87–90, 1996.
11. Lamont, A., James Clerk Maxwell (1831–1879), *Creation* **15**(3):45–47, June 1993; creation.com/maxwell.
12. Doyle, S., Einstein's heroes: biblical creationists, *Creation* **36**(1):54–55, 2014.
13. Woodmorappe, J., Lord Kelvin revisited on the young age of the earth, *Journal of Creation* **13**(1):14, April 1999; creation.com/kelvin.
14. Fox, W., André Marie Ampère; in: *The Catholic Encyclopedia*, Robert Appleton Company, New York, 1907; newadvent.org, acc. 4 December 2012.
15. Lamont, A., Great creation scientist: Blaise Pascal (1623–1662): Outstanding scientist and committed Christian, *Creation* **20** (1):38–39, 1997; creation.com/pascal.
16. Lamont, A., James Joule: The great experimenter who was guided by God, *Creation* **15**(2):47–50,1993; creation.com/joule.
17. Lamont, A., Louis Pasteur (1822–1895): Outstanding scientist and opponent of evolution, *Creation* **14**(1):16–19, 1991; creation.com/pasteur.
18. Grigg, R., Mercator's projection, *Creation* **38**(1):54–55, 2016.
19. Lamont, A., Michael Faraday—God's power and electric power, *Creation* **12**(4):22–24, 1990; creation.com/faraday.
20. Sarfati, J., The biblical roots of modern science, *Creation* **32**(4):32–36, 2010; creation.com/roots. Atheists doing science successfully today, whether or not making great discoveries, are doing so under what were originally biblical assumptions.

JAMES CLERK MAXWELL

ANDRÉ-MARIE AMPÈRE

JAMES JOULE

BLAISE PASCAL

THE GAP THEORY—

■ **Henry M. Morris**

"In the beginning, God created the heavens and the earth" (Genesis 1:1).

"The earth was without form and void, and darkness was over the face of the deep. And the Spirit of God was hovering over the face of the waters" (Genesis 1:2).

MANY PEOPLE assume there is a great gap in time between Genesis 1:1 and Genesis 1:2. Most of these do this to accommodate the geological age system of billions of years of supposed earth history in the Genesis record of creation. The idea is something like this: billions of years ago God created the space-mass-time universe, then the geological ages took place over billions of years of earth history. Different forms of life developed, now preserved in the fossil record. These life-forms represent those ages—the invertebrates of the Cambrian Period, the dinosaurs of the Cretaceous Period ... finally the mammals, birds and 'ape-men' of the Tertiary Period—just before the recent epoch.

Then the idea is that, at the end of these geological ages, a great cataclysm took place on earth, with Satan having rebelled in heaven and many of the angels following him in that rebellion. God, therefore, cast him to the earth, and the earth underwent a great cataclysm, leaving it finally without form and void, and with darkness on the face of the deep, as described in Genesis 1:2.

Subsequently, according to this idea—usually known as the gap theory—God then re-created or reconstituted the earth in the six literal days of creation recorded in the first chapter of Genesis. The argument for this theory makes verse two read, "The earth *became* without form and void" (some would render it "The earth became waste and desolate"), as though it had previously been a beautiful world. But now, because of the cataclysm, it was a devastated remnant of a world, so that there was a change of condition. It became without form and void.

'Was' Means 'Was'

A significant problem with this idea is that the Hebrew word for 'was' really should be translated 'was'. It should not be translated 'became'. It is the Hebrew verb of being, *hayah*, and normally it is simply translated 'was'. In all the standard translations of the Old Testament, that is the way this verse is rendered.

On some occasions, in an unusual situation if the context requires it, the word can be translated 'became'. But this requires the verb *hayah* to be followed by the preposition 'to' (Hebrew *le*). *This is not the case in Genesis 1:2.*

Some people use Isaiah 45:18 as an argument for the use of 'became' in Genesis 1:2. In this verse, Isaiah says that God created the earth not in vain. He formed it to be inhabited. The word 'in vain' is the same as *tohu*; that is, the same word translated 'without form' in Genesis 1:2. So gap theorists say that since God

did not create it that way, it must have become that way. But again, the context is significant. In Isaiah, the context requires the use of the translation 'in vain'. That is, God did not create the earth without a purpose; He created it to be inhabited. Genesis 1 tells us then how He brought form to the unformed earth and inhabitants to the empty earth. It was not really finished until He said so at the end of the six days of creation.

The word *tohu* is actually translated 10 different ways in about 20 occurrences in the Old Testament. Isaiah 45:19 has the same word, and there it has to be translated 'vainly' or 'in vain'. It is also proper to translate it that way in Isaiah 45:18. It depends on the context as to how it is to be precisely translated. In Genesis 1:2 the context simply indicates the earth had no structure as yet. It was unformed; it was not even spherical at that point, but was comprised of only the basic elements of earth material.

Sequence

Furthermore, it is important to note that Genesis 1, like all Hebrew historical narrative, is full of a type of verb called the *waw consecutive*, with the Hebrew letter *waw* (ו) attached to a *verb*. This introduces most verses of Genesis 1, teaching a *sequence of actions*. There was this

AN IDEA WITH HOLES?

happening, and then this happened, and then this happened, and then this … each following directly upon the other.

However, Genesis 1:2 has a different construction, called the *waw disjunctive*, where the *waw* is connected to a *noun*. This is a parenthetical statement, describing the condition in which the earth was created, not something it became. We can compare other cases in Scripture:

- Judges 8:11 says that Gideon attacked a Midianite army that "felt secure", which in Hebrew is *hāyāh betah*, literally 'was unsuspecting',

which obviously was describing the condition of the army. If the gap theorists were right, it would entail that Midianites 'became' unsuspecting *after* Gideon attacked.

- Jonah 3:3 reads, "So Jonah arose and went to Nineveh … Now Nineveh was [*hāyᵊtāh*] an exceedingly great city." A consistent gap theorist would need to interpret this Jonah arrived, then Nineveh 'became' exceedingly great.

Another argument of those who advocate the gap theory is that the word 'darkness' suggests that something is wrong with the creation. But Isaiah 45:7 says that God created the darkness. In order for there to be day and night, which was necessary for the further activity of God and man upon the earth, there must be day and night. So God actually had to create darkness. Thus, there is nothing implicitly wrong with it being dark. God created it that way. Darkness later came to represent, in some contexts, a symbol of evil—as opposed to light—since "God is light and in Him is no darkness at all" (1 John 1:5). But in the context here, there is no evil connotation suggested.

On the other hand, there are many overwhelming difficulties with the gap theory, and we really should not accept this as the interpretation of Genesis 1:2. The idea that the geological ages took place in between Genesis 1:1 and 1:2 is precluded by the plain biblical statement in the Ten Commandments, where God said, "For in six days the LORD made heaven and earth, the sea, and all that is in them, and rested on the seventh day" (Exodus 20:11). That is, He was telling man that he must work six days and rest one day because God worked six days and rested one day. The context goes on to say that *everything* in heaven and earth and in the sea—the entire created order—was made in six days. There could

THE GAP?

Millions or billions of years

Geologic layers and fossils laid down in Lucifer's Flood

have been nothing left over that was not made during the six days (including the angelic realm).

The gap theory, on the other hand, would require that only the surface of the earth was reconstituted in the six days. The earth's core, the basic structure, the great fossil beds containing the remnants of the dinosaurs, and so on, all of this would predate the six days of Creation. But God says specifically that everything in the earth and in the heavens and in the sea was made in the six days.

Death Before Sin?

Theologically, there is also a very grave difficulty with the gap theory. The Bible says there was no sin or death until man brought them into the world. According to the gap theory, however, there had already been billions of years of suffering and death in the world, represented by the fossils and the sedimentary rocks of the earth's crust, which are now supposed to identify the geological ages. According to the gap theory, at the end of the geological ages Satan sinned and was cast to the earth, and then there was a great cataclysm, so that the geological ages with billions of years of suffering and death took place before Satan sinned and certainly before man sinned.

The Bible, on the other hand, says specifically, "sin came into the world through one man, and death through sin" (Romans 5:12), so that there was no death in the world until man brought sin into it. Death is also called "the last enemy"

(1 Corinthians 15:26). The gap theory would require billions of years of animal suffering (and hundreds of thousands of years of human suffering) in the world before man or even Satan had sinned. That would make God the author of sin. So the gap theory is precluded theologically.

Non-Science

Scientifically, it won't work either, because the whole essence of the geological age system, which some people try to accommodate by the gap theory, is based on what geologists call 'uniformitarianism'. That is, the continuity of processes in the ancient world with those in the modern world. The very structure of the geological age system is based on the assumption that present rates and processes are the same as those that took place in the past. There is no room for a world-wide cataclysm interrupting those processes in the system of the geological ages.

That is why no geologist would ever accept the gap theory. In order to have a world-wide cataclysm that would destroy all the pre-cataclysm mountains and cast them into the sea, so that there was the deep everywhere, and then blow billions of tons of debris up into the sky so that there was darkness over the deep everywhere, as Genesis 1:2 describes it, it would have to be a world-wide nuclear explosion, or volcanic explosion, or something which would literally disintegrate the crust of the earth where the fossils and the sedimentary rocks are that identify the

geological ages. So the gap theory would destroy the evidence for the geological ages in order to accommodate them! It is a self-negating theory scientifically; it creates overwhelming scientific problems.

Therefore, we have to reject the gap theory as an interpretation of Genesis 1:2. We can be confident that a simple and straightforward, literal interpretation of the biblical record will satisfy all the real facts of geology. ∎

HENRY M. MORRIS (1918–2006) B.S., M.S., Ph.D.
Formerly Professor of Hydrogeology at Virginia Polytechnic University, Dr Morris was respected in engineering circles for his textbook Applied Hydraulics in Engineering. *In 1961 he co-authored (with Dr John Whitcomb) the 1961 book* The Genesis Flood, *launching the modern creationist movement. He was founding president of the Institute for Creation Research, a co-founder of the Creation Research Society, and wrote more than 60 books defending the Bible. For more: creation.com/ henry-m-morris.*

Article from
Creation **10**(1):35–37
December 1987

HERE'S GOOD NEWS FOR THE WORLD

Creation Ministries International *seeks to give glory and honour to the triune God of the Bible as Creator, and to affirm the truth of the biblical record of the real origin and history of the world and mankind.*

Part of this real history is the bad news that the rebellion of the first man, Adam, against God's command, brought death, suffering, and separation from God into this world. We see the results all around us. All of Adam's descendants are sinful from conception (Psalm 51:5) and have themselves entered into this rebellion (sin). They therefore cannot live with a holy God, but are condemned to separation from God. The Bible says that "all have sinned, and come short of the glory of God" (Romans 3:23) and that all are therefore subject to "everlasting destruction from the presence of the Lord and from the glory of His power" (2 Thessalonians 1:9).

But the good news is that God has done something about it. "For God so loved the world, that He gave His only begotten Son, that whoever believes in Him should not perish, but have everlasting life" (John 3:16).

Jesus Christ the Creator, God the Son, though totally sinless, took on human nature, so He could become our Redeemer. Then He suffered, on behalf of mankind, the penalty of mankind's sin, which is death and separation from God. He did this to satisfy the righteous demands of the holiness and justice of God, His Father. Jesus was the perfect sacrifice; He died on a cross, but on the third day, He rose again, conquering death, so that all who truly believe in Him, repent (repentance = a change of mind) of their sin and trust in Him (rather than their own merit), are able to come back to God and live for eternity with their Creator.

Therefore: "He who believes on Him is not condemned, but he who does not believe is condemned already, because he has not believed in the name of the only-begotten Son of God" (John 3:18).

What a wonderful Saviour—and what a wonderful salvation in Christ our Creator!

If you want to know more of what the Bible says about how you can receive eternal life, please contact a *Creation Ministries International* office near you.

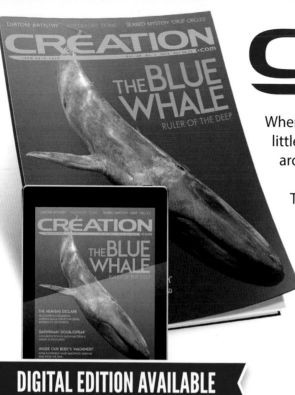

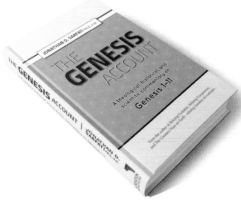